A GUIDE TO

PREVENTIVE CHILD PSYCHIATRY

the art of parenthood

A GUIDE TO
PREVENTIVE CHILD PSYCHIATRY

the art of parenthood

HENRY H. WORK, M.D.
Associate Professor of Psychiatry
and
JUSTIN D. CALL. M.D.
Associate Professor of Psychiatry

School of Medicine
University of California at Los Angeles
Los Angeles, California

The Blakiston Division
McGRAW-HILL BOOK COMPANY
New York • Toronto • Sydney • London

TO GINNY AND BARBARA

PREFACE

Children grow. This not remarkable fact provides the base for this book. We have tried to put together a body of knowledge about the growth of children and their changing relations with their parents which will fit the needs of the practitioner who will deal with them. We are well aware that to be of assistance to a child and to his parents is not a simple process. Even more so, we are impressed with the scantiness of the preparation in our society for this major job. Parents find themselves expected to do the major job of child rearing with a training that may be skimpy or non-existent. More and more individual pairs find themselves in the category of parents at relatively tender years. While it is hard to grow up in America without schooling, this does not normally include the art of parenthood.

Perhaps this art cannot be taught. It would be difficult to devise a curriculum that would cover the manifold relations that comprise a growing life. It would be even more difficult to do so in a manner that would embrace all the feelings accompanying this process, since these facets of growth are more obscure.

We have tried to look at the overall growth of a child. A six-month-old child may sleep poorly. A two-year-old may have constant temper tantrums. A seven-year-old may find difficulty in learning to read. A teenager rebels. All of these things may happen to different children or they may at any one time be a part of one child's growth. In devising a book to help understand the physician's role in the process of growth, we have tried to make clear the manner in which any one phase of growth builds on preceding phases. It is our feeling that symptoms are not isolated, but they continually depend on something that has happened before in the interaction of the child and his environment.

We have planned this book for the physician who practices pediatric medicine. We have tried to describe both the normal and abnormal growth of the child and the corresponding growth that occurs in the parents who are rearing him. We feel that it should be possible to understand from this the *developmental meaning* of symptoms. This is not a book of psychotherapy. Rather, it is one that demonstrates the potential of the child for illness or health and the role of the physician in maintaining this health. It is hoped that we have offered an adequate picture of children and their parents, as well as certain of the potential difficulties that they may have, so that preventive steps may be taken to avoid on-going difficulties as well as future pitfalls.

Henry H. Work, M.D.
Justin D. Call, M.D.

CONTENTS

ix

Part IV   Special Problems

PART I

INTRODUCTION

THE PROBLEM

THE CARE OF CHILDREN TODAY

It has been no idle boast in pediatrics that from earliest times this discipline has been devoted to "the welfare of children." To determine at all times what is best for such welfare has not always been easy. Other disciplines within the medical profession have at times scorned the efforts of these physicians and at best have been condescending about what they call "medicine for little people." There are those within our own profession who feel that there is nothing unique in the care of the child. Such scorn may come from a variety of specialists who feel that they know more about a particular part of the growing individual. It may come from colleagues dealing with the adult who feel that the child merely mirrors the pathological processes of the grown organism.

To miss, however, the overwhelming impact that growth and change makes in disease processes is to avoid both the value and joy of the practice of dealing with children. Indeed, it can be pointed out that the factor of growth is in itself an awesome process containing so many unknowns that it provides fear for those who are accustomed to dealing with the fixed, stable, and organized disease processes of the mature individual.

For centuries medicine conspicuously shunned the child. It was not until major knowledge in the fields of infection and nutrition made it possible to understand the growth process that pediatrics came into its own. Yet, in a way, both of these major areas of concern made it possible to neglect the child in his inherent totality. The abrupt and often lethal course of infections made it possible to look at the diseases of childhood more than the child with disease. Concerns about nutrition made it possible to think of the child as a tube into which various foodstuffs could be poured without any reckoning of the meaning of this food to those who put it there and the child who received it.

Curiously, the extreme concerns that physicians devoted to children expressed about the content and organization of the child's dietary needs actually have led to a series of problems of eating that plague children in their later years. Perhaps it was not until the various infections had been subdued, if not conquered, that it became possible to look at the child who received all this food and to begin to wonder how he operated, what the meaning of his growth was, and what the relationship of such things as eating, sleeping, and general activity meant to his growth process.

To be sure, there were prophets who bespoke the need to consider the varied aspects of child life. Unfortunately, it was all too easy to become sequestered in a specific area of interest about children and to neglect that which had to do with the making of his personality. Yet, Paundler in Europe and Aldrich in this country pronounced a gospel that linked together not only a host of the child's activities, but the child's relation to the world at large.

The American pediatric debt to Aldrich is not easy to measure. It is worth considering, however, that he considered the area of feeding not only in its own right, but also as an area which enabled him to put the child into some sort of a perspective so that he could be thought of as an individual. Aldrich did more than merely stress that we were feeding old-fashioned children in a modern world. He took the commonplace fact of eating and pointed out its central nature in the life of the growing child, its crucial importance in linking the child to the outside world, its

Fig. 1-1. An infant requires a source of security while exploring the outer world.

relevance to growth through nutrition and ultimately its impact on the personality of the child as he developed. At a time when clinics were beseiged with mothers uttering the plaintive plea, "Doctor, he won't eat," Aldrich showed that the very process of feeding had led to this moment of anxiety and the plea on the part of the parents. He related to us that the very parent who uttered this sad complaint was the one who had, at times under medical pressure, force-fed her infant to the point that the child had utterly given up and no longer desired to fulfill mother's and doctor's need to stuff himself.

Fig. 1-2. Establishment of independent patterns of feeding is a crucial step in the child's development.

This intricate combination of nutritional advice, parental pressure, and childhood resistance opened up a chapter in pediatrics that made "the welfare" of children truly a realistic phenomenon. It was at this point that the growing field of child psychiatry could merge with the parallel concern of the pediatrician for the child and a composite science could be evolved. Prevention which had been so integral in the pediatric science of infectious diseases could then begin to be applied to the totality of the child in his intimate and curious relationships with the world around him.

THE WIDENING SCOPE

These changes which have come about in the practice of pediatrics with the advances in knowledge about the behavioral, emotional, and personality difficulties in children have been urged along by two major pressures. One has been the change in the disease picture of children so that the rare, the bizarre, and the unusual in medical pediatrics is no longer so frequently seen. It is unfortunate that a good deal of training in pediatrics still centers around conditions which, at times, occupy hospital beds but which are rarely encountered in an ongoing practice.

The other major force in changing pediatric activity has been demonstrated in the expectations of the parents. The coming of newer knowledge concerning the psychology of childhood has not been uniquely a concern of the medical press. Just as pediatrics has grown up in the present century, the same century has seen a vast publicity concerning children and their problems, as well as parents and their problems. Thus expectations of what is to be offered in the pediatrician's office have greatly changed.

There is still a feeling among both practitioners and educators that the education of the pediatrician includes an overtraining in certain highly specialized technical aspects of pediatrics but does not prepare the pediatrician for certain common problems of his practice. It also appears that the teaching of the psychologic aspects of medical practice and pediatric practice is not as well organized nor understood as are the teaching aspects of other parts of medical care. Such discrepancies in teaching are reflected in a variety of job situations met in office practice, bedside practice, home practice, and so forth. At times, it appears that the pediatrician must be all things to all people. It is not so much that there is more work to be done in pediatrics, but there are more diversified kinds of work to be done. Sometimes the pediatrician may feel engulfed not only by the inadequacies of his training, but also by a lack of hands to carry out the task itself.

Conflict, therefore, exists not only between training and practice, but between the goal of the student in training and the expectations of the physician in his practice. In addition, patients no longer expect all of the services that they need from one physician alone. Rather they have grown used to a physician having allies of various sorts. Not every physician approves of the use of allied professions, but it should be considered, when the burdens of the job become onerous, that there may very well be people who can share in the task: the social worker, the psychologist, the educator, other medical practitioners, and so on. A wide range of knowledge is encompassed in the psychologic care of children, and not all of it is the property of the medical profession.

Perhaps more important for the individual physician, the problem of distribution of time becomes important. It can be said here very clearly that as far as psychologic problems are concerned, the earlier they are investigated, the more medical time can be conserved. It may well be that the balance of time utilized in the practice of general pediatrics may need exploration. Certain studies in recent years have suggested that the amount of time spent on physical examinations, especially repetitive examinations, can be modified. The savings can be used for more direct counseling and discussion with the parents.

In addition, overemphasis on organic symptomatology can lead to anxiety on the part of parents, induced by overexamination and extended exploration of symptoms. It might be more profitable to consider the use of such time for gaining a greater understanding of the patient's concern about the symptom and seeking to discover what are the roots of this symptom as opposed to its manifestations.

As an example of this type of time-saving operation, certain physicians have discovered that it is profitable to set aside days or parts of days when they confer only with parents. It is felt that this type of conference with the parents of a small child can more easily (in the absence of the child) evoke feelings about training and handling that can be modified in a preventive fashion. Later chapters will attempt to discuss the manner in which this is done, but it is important to remember that one cannot modify psychologic phenomenon without understanding specifically what in such a phenomenon is bothering the parent.

The newer interest in genetic problems of children, as well as in the specific difficulties that arise in families due to mental retardation, demand a changed focus of the physician's attention. In such patients certain things have occurred and attitudes are established. Lest they become of significance and a problem to the family, the anxieties and concerns of the parents about genetic errors and about conditions of intelligence in their child will warrant both investigation and a continued understanding. This will be discussed in detail in the chapter concerning mental retardation. Nothing has changed in pediatric practice so far as the concern for the child is involved. What has changed is an increase of the tools that derive from knowledge and the impact of this knowledge on both the practice and the expectations as far as the families are concerned.

IS THERE A PREVENTION?

The idea that there could be a preventive approach to the behavioral difficulties of children has not always been easy to sustain. One of the purposes of this text is to suggest that if such a prevention is possible, it can be realized only on the basis of using a consistent concept of the growth process. The other base for such prevention lies in the fact that the opportunity for such prevention is in the hands of the physician who has an opportunity to follow the child and be an advisor to the family on the child's health over a relatively long period of time. As we have discussed, the field of pediatrics has the advantage of having a number of internal critics who suggest that the practice of pediatrics is changing and that much of the change has to do with a widening recognition of the social and emotional conditions of children. It seems appropriate to comment here that if there is to be an expansion of the modes of dealing with children, then not only fundamental observations of growth are important, but attitudes toward growth and the developmental process are equally important.

Will He Grow Out Of It? A very common (but we feel erroneous) attitude toward growth is based on the idea that children pass through various stages or phases and that these areas of growth are self-limited. This attitude optimistically assumes that if the child has difficulty in any one phase of growth, the mere succession to the next phase will suffice to heal the difficulties that have occurred during the previous one. A pediatrician without optimism would not be a good pediatrician. Thus, it would be wrong to begin a book by suggesting that optimism is an overvalued

Fig. 1-3. Will he grow out of it?

tool for a physician to use in his practice of dealing with children. At the same time, it would be erroneous not to point out that the psychiatrist's concept of growth is rather different. It includes the specific idea that difficulties occurring in any one phase of growth tend to affect all subsequent stages of growth and in a rather predictable fashion.

As we will describe in detail subsequently, psychiatric conditions in childhood rarely present themselves as emergencies or even as acute situations. It is more frequently obvious that the pattern of behavior in many children who come for psychiatric help has been constant over a period of time and that the difficulties they demonstrate are discernible much earlier than would seem to be apparent in the actual referral. The specific case material in this book will demonstrate two factors involved in this situation. One concerns an appreciation of the process of growth; the other, a reluctance on the part of parents and some physicians to see pathology in children and to do something about it at an early stage.

This book will be based on current studies of development which consistently suggest that the process of growth is an ever-building one. Children do not only grow like flowers, blossoming out from within, but they grow and develop in relationship to the outside world and particularly in relationship to other human beings. This is especially true of those with whom they have close contacts, such as their parents. Furthermore, we will demonstrate that there are certain critical phases in this growth process: the need for security in the early years, the need for control as the child begins to grow and become independent, the need to understand his relationship with his peers as he goes through early childhood, the manner of his participation in schooling, and the dramatic struggle of establishing his identity in the adolescent period.

There was a time in psychiatric thinking when great concern was expressed about the scars left by conflicts arising in early periods of life. At the present time, there is less worry about the scars than about the manner in which such conflicts modify the

Fig. 1-4. Children not only blossom but also need nourishment.

child's approach to succeeding phases of development. One important consideration in understanding the process that brings about behavioral difficulties is to be aware of the presence of pathology in young family situations as well as in young children.

It is our impression that the unwillingness to pin a label of difficulty on a growing child still greatly affects that part of our practice which deals with the behavior of children and our parental guidance. When parents come to us complaining about disordered behavior in their children, an early tendency is to make an optimistic assumption that this is going to change with the growth process. Physicians interested in children very naturally become allies of the child and are often for this reason rather indifferent to the anxieties of the parents about behavioral phenomenon which children demonstrate.

Much has been written over the years about the concept of iatrogenic disease. In pediatric practice, this may take the form of an exaggeration of physical symptomatology by physicians because of their own natural interest in organic pathology. This may cause undue anxiety in parents. However, there is a contrary observation that many physicians dealing with children tend to minimize behavioral difficulties and resort to a considerable amount of reassurance in order to make the difficulty go away as if by magic.

A medical student who had followed a case seen in the pediatric clinic over into observation in a psychiatric clinic commented as follows concerning his psychiatric supervisor:

I was struck by the difference between his very poor prognosis for my case, the social worker's doubtful prognosis, and the pediatrician's optimistic outlook.

There will be no effort in this book to suggest that behavioral difficulties quickly respond to simple therapeutic measures. We will demonstrate, however, that a knowledge of growth and development and the role that the family plays in this process is fundamental to the resolution of such difficulties. In addition, we do not suggest that parents are happy about having conflictual situations looked into. At times, looking at the core of a situation may lead physicians into conflicts with parents.

It is, however, as important to make a positive diagnosis in the field of behavioral pathology as it is in the field of organic pathology. Much time is spent in the physician's office in ruling out various causes for an underlying basic symptom. At times this prolongs the diagnostic process, which in itself enhances the disease situation. We all obtain comfort in our approach to families by going through a diagnostic survey and ruling out a variety of known conditions. Sometimes, however, we take too much comfort in such a process because it leads us to the feeling that we have eliminated everything that is important.

The child who comes in complaining of abdominal pain presents us with an opportunity for such a diagnostic survey. Once we have eliminated major indications for surgery and major indications for medical therapeusis, we feel comfortable in saying that the disease is functional. Yet the child who complains today of abdominal pain may be attempting to communicate to the parents, the school, and to us about a specifically stressful external or internal situation, about which something could be done now. Lack of appropriate intervention may lead to a buildup of neurotic symptomatology to the point where he may later present severe hypochondriasis, psychosomatic complaints, or a syndrome such as school phobia.

One of our problems in approaching the behavioral disorders of children is the unacknowledged assumption that these manifestations are not true indices of disease but merely reflect something to do with the goodness or badness of children, their parents, or their social background. We will discuss this at greater length, but it is important at this time to realize that the various dichotomies of good and bad, clean and dirty, sick and healthy are not in themselves true or useful standards for evaluating the mass of symptomatology that presents itself in our offices.

A second important deterrent to adequate diagnostic procedure is our investment in the patient. This may be as simple as our desire not to annoy a mother who has been a good patient. It may be as complex as our feeling that since we have taken care of a patient over a long period of time, things must be going well. There is a general feeling with our long-term patients that everything we have done for them is to their advantage and, therefore, if the case is going badly there must be some mistake they are making that relates neither to our diagnostic skill nor to our therapeutic endeavor. If we are to apply our knowledge of development, we must observe our patients with the same skill that is used in making observations of other clinical situations. We cannot be misled by our investment in the progress of the patient.

If psychiatrists are at times pessimistic about the onset of behavioral difficulties, it is not merely because of the vast increase in emotional and mental maladies, but because the frame of observing emotional development is different from the frame used in the observation of physical growth. We will demonstrate that the observation of emotional growth includes not only critical phases but the reduplication and recapitulation of early difficulties in later periods. For these reasons, a stormy second year or a stormy fifth year may often presage difficulties as the child enters the arena of adolescence, when growth processes and sexual concerns which were seen in the early years once more begin to flower.

Equally, it will be important to recognize that the very valuable tool of reassurance may in itself be at times a handicap. The application of this powerful tool alleviates symptoms. These same symptoms may well go underground if the basic conflict is not understood and removed. They may equally well reappear in a succeeding developmental phase. A retrospective view of emotional disorders of adults suggests an everlasting building during the phases of maturation. Whenever we see an excessive number of symptoms developing in a child, whenever we see modifications in the developmental process, we must be alert to continue a cumulative sort of observation. Just as the knowledge of development has come out of increased interest in the dynamics of the progress of growth, so increased diagnostic and prognostic skill will arise, not from a dismissal of symptoms, not from an assumption that certain states of behavior are encapsulated and different in themselves, but rather from an understanding that the behavioral difficulties at any period in growth have a cumulative effect and become transformed as the organism grows.

The pediatrician must be an ally of the child, but it is equally important to note that children are neither loaded with original sin nor continually "trailing clouds of glory."

At this point an example of developing symptoms is appropriate:

Norman was the first-born child of intelligent, accomplished parents. He was planned for but born early in the father's career while the parents were living in the East. He was a full-term baby, healthy in every respect and was described as being happy, alert, and active. His mother felt that she did not have enough milk to breast-feed him, so he was bottle-fed. He had colic until the age of three months, for which a darkened room was prescribed. In the first few months of life he seemed especially sensitive to the noise of the piano and would stop crying if he heard such a noise. His mother was tense, frightened, and somewhat depressed with her first child and felt as though she didn't quite know how to satisfy him.

Fig. 1-5. "Neither loaded with original sin or trailing clouds of glory."

Comment. At this point in Norman's history, pediatric examination would easily have revealed the above. The thing that would not be easily revealed and probably was not revealed was the mother's feeling of tiredness, anxiety, and depression in handling her child. If it had been acknowledged, some additional support of her maternal role might have been achieved, both through direct efforts on the part of the physician and through helping her busy husband acquaint himself with the family situation.

Norman remained an active, wiry, and somewhat tense child. He smiled but often also stared at his mother. He became afraid to go to sleep at night without the light on at about the age of two. This fear persisted through his early years. There were several moves by the family between the age of eight months and five years due to the unsettled nature of the father's occupation.

Norman's development was quite rapid. He sat at four months and walked with minimal holding-on at eight months. He was able to speak in brief sentences at fourteen months. He was quite outgoing and, as the mother said, "into everything." The mother continued being quite perplexed in how to manage him. A new sibling was born at age three and another at age five. Intense rivalry developed shortly after the birth of the sibling at three.

Comment. The earlier tenseness, shown by colic and sensitivity to environmental stimulation, had now taken form as fearfulness and rivalry, with some evidences of a faulty adaptation to the larger social environment. The mother's insecurity in taking care of the small child was again manifest at this period in terms of her inability to know what to do about the rivalry and his fearfulness. The estrangement which the mother felt as a result of her own depression had now continued even though her depression had lifted. Later it was discovered that this depressive feeling was as much due to her feeling about her husband being so busy as it was to the new burdens of motherhood.

Norman was referred for psychiatric consultation at the age of eight because of eye blinking, head-shaking movements, unusual voice sounds, grimacing, and unusual hand movements. Bed wetting had been present from the age of four until the age of eight, occurring once or twice each night, and Norman was beginning to say such things as, "I wish I were dead." All of this had become worse since the family's recent move at the age of five, at which time Norman felt uprooted from friends that he had in the neighborhood. The first eye blinking and head-shaking movements which were the beginning of the "tics" occurred one afternoon when his mother told him not to go outside without a hat on. He defied her, went to a baseball game, and shook his head to see if he was getting a headache. It became a pleasurable activity for him and later he said that he needed to have his "habits" because they were a source of pleasure to him. Also, it was learned that the father's method of discipline had consisted of spanking whenever he lost his temper. Norman had become somewhat defiant and obstructionistic, although he had done well in school. He was preoccupied with television shows of violence, read the newspaper about accidents, and had himself been subjected to the bullying of older boys in a new and unfamiliar neighborhood following the move. He preferred girls to his male peers. His speech difficulty, consisting of unusual voice-cracking sounds, accompanied the tics along with grotesque facial expressions. Meanwhile, Norman had begun to teach himself the piano. His mother had played the piano and he seemed to be learning very rapidly by himself.

Comment. At this stage in Norman's development, the early fearfulness which he showed and the estrangement which had been present with the mother became converted to the social situation. His loss of a valued friend and the fear of the bullying boys was enhanced when the father emerged as a threatening rather than supporting figure for him. A new trend began showing itself in his personality, namely a passivity, a withdrawal from others and a search for gratifying personal experiences not involving people. These included both the tic and the piano playing. He was obviously afraid but of different things now and at a different social level. His earlier sensitivity to stimuli and the lack of the mother to form a bulwark against the stimuli had been compensated for in Norman by defensive withdrawal. The etiology of the tic and facial grimaces was found to have its origin in his inability to manage his deep aggressive and destructive impulses which had been overwhelming for him.

There had been a consistent but transforming series of symptoms since early infancy. Experience in working with families with such problems suggests that they are easier to change earlier than later. Recognition and response to all the various aspects of the family situation provide the key to such changes.

ATTITUDES

The preceding section has suggested that there may be fundamental differences in attitudes and approaches between physicians
whose time is spent mostly with children. The pediatrician and the
child psychiatrist have an equal opportunity to see growth, but
they may view it quite differently. It is well, at this point, to list
certain assumptions which may reflect differing attitudes and
therefore different modes of approach.

1. *Babies are a lot sturdier than people think.* To some extent,
this attitude grows out of the history of pediatrics wherein, along
with good public health care, there has been a remarkable reduction of infantile mortality rates, decreases in premature morbidity,
and a much earlier approach to the congenital defects of infancy.
Every physician who cares for children has seen the growth of a
frail, helpless-looking infant into a robust year-old child. Such a
daily reminder suggests that "babies do grow up" and "there is a
strong, healthy trend in each individual to achieve more mature
levels of development."

2. *Children can withstand traumatic physical or psychological
insult better than most adults.* This concept is supported by some
of the dramatically demonstrated infantile capacities to withstand
surgery with a viability, resiliency, and adaptability possible only
in the young organism. Even the infectious diseases tend to run
their course quickly. More recently we have seen the blossoming
of a deprived child in the hospital with appropriate substitute
mothering. The assumption is further supported by the occasional
dramatic return to normal of a sick toxic child. The dramatic
quality of all of these quick responses supports and gives clinical
evidence to the assumption that children have a greater capacity
to withstand insult than do older individuals.

3. *Mothers worry too much about little things. They should be
reassured about almost anything since that will make them more
secure as parents and therefore better for their children.* It is not
surprising that a pediatrician, facing daily the anxious concerns of
mothers, develops the concept that worries are not only multiple
but most of the time minor. Such concerns in the puerperium as,

"What is that little rash on his face?"; "Does he see anything?"; "Are you sure that he hears?"; "His feet look so funny"; or, in an eight-month-old, "He's been crying a lot at night recently"; or in a one-year-old, "His appetite's falling off"—all of these concerns, which at times seem very superficial, add up to the concept that worry is the normal phenomenon of life and that the mother who does not worry must be a very strange individual.

4. *Certain behavioral traits change rapidly.* Whenever the physician is confronted with an example of minor or major intercurrent disease, he sees accompanying it periods of rapid regression in children. In addition, the physician frequently watches the rapid recoveries from such regressions. The regression of an infant with the arrival of a new sibling is quite characteristic. It is almost predictable in many instances. The pediatrician, in fact, can frequently predict in a given instance what form the regression will take, how long it will last, and how it can be resolved. It is thus possible to aid a mother through such a difficult period. Many fears, such as, for example, fear of strangers and separation, brief phobic attitudes toward play objects, restless sleep, calling out for mother, minor eating difficulties, temper tantrums at a certain age, are all to be expected in the normal process of growth. One is, in fact, frequently surprised at children who manifest none of these common difficulties. So common are they that their description, bolstered by certain interpretations, has become a school of psychologic thought in this country. This suggests phase-limited behavior and promotes the idea of great reassurance. Such compendiums of reassurance, however, are not always suitable to the individual child, even though the comfort they contain fits large groups of children.

5. *There is a strong and healthy trend toward maturation in all children.* The fact of growth itself suggests that everything is going to change with increases in size, shape, and weight. It would follow that psychological development would necessarily follow the same drive toward maturation.

Studies of psychological development of children and the

growth of the personality have led child psychiatrists to adopt certain differing opinions about these very same assumptions.

1. *Early experiences have a great influence upon later pathology.* As we shall describe, certain children who have suffered various degrees of deprivation early in infancy demonstrate in their continuing development states of apathy, disinterest, and withdrawal which seem very dependent upon the initial insult. The studies of Goldfarb, Beres, Rhinegold, Provence, and Spitz support the thesis that, sturdy as infants are, they need a variety of stimuli over and above good nutrition and care to enable them to mature in a comfortable fashion. The histories of adults with schizophrenia, as well as certain neurotic disorders, are filled with disturbances in the early months of life and suggest to the child psychiatrist that early deprivation is a very crucial factor in forming the personality, even in a child who is physiologically quite sturdy. Babies may be sturdy, but they also are very impressionable, and the results of early experience may not be manifest until much later.

2. *The earlier the experience of either deprivation or trauma, the more general will be its effect.* This, the so-called epigenetic view of development, translates the physiologic knowledge of embryology into the psychologic knowledge of development. Erikson, who has most thoroughly described this developmental process, makes clear the difference between conflictual situations which occur at different stages of life and, therefore, have differing effects both in quality and quantity. These will be discussed in detail in the individual chapters concerning development.

3. *Parents often worry too much about the wrong thing and too little about what counts.* For many parents, the daily tasks of caring for the child and addressing oneself to the surface phenomena of such care become all-absorbing and make it difficult for them to communicate with the physician about anything but these daily concerns. These concerns are not necessarily best met by reassurance. As many physicians know, such reassurance is very often about as effective as treating pneumonia with cough medicine. Many important aspects of the child's development and environ-

mental experience may never be mentioned by the mother. We have repeatedly observed in the histories of psychotic youngsters, for example, the history of bizarre play activities, excessive rocking or head banging, indifference to people or treating them as objects rather than persons, none of these symptoms having been mentioned or considered important by the parent except in retrospect (see also the following case illustration). A mother may spend a long time with her pediatrician discussing a child's physical growth, his patterns of eating, elimination, and behavior, without mentioning the nature of her household help and the relationship of this help to her child, or without bringing up for discussion plans for care of the child during parental vacations or trips. One of the most frequent concerns of parents is that the skin of the child be unblemished. This is daily demonstrated in a variety of questions about small rashes, spots, etc., which seem to be sources of anxiety to the parent. Perhaps some brief illustrations will suffice.

The mother of a child who later became autistic had had feelings of revulsion, disgust, and fear of handling this child as an infant because of a rather small birthmark on the shoulder. While she had called her pediatrician's attention to the birthmark and he had reassured her about its going away in time, she had never shared with him the feelings which were aroused in her by the birthmark. In subsequent visits with the mother it was learned that her feelings about the birthmark were related to her guilt about having damaged the child and her fear of doing more damage. The relationship between mother and child was filled with guilt, estrangement, and physical detachment. As a result, a serious affectional estrangement developed between the mother and the child which laid the foundation for the child's atypical development.

In another autistic youngster seen at the age of seventeen months, the mother had been unable to establish a close relationship with the child because of the dirtiness associated with the special feeding procedures required because of a congenital cleft palate. Again the nature of the defect had been recognized and early surgery had been performed, but the mother's feelings in dealing with the defect had not been recognized. A very rapid and good therapeutic effect resulted after this particular aspect of the mother's concern could be specifically dealt with in interviews with her and the father. It is quite likely that the estrangement that developed between the mother and the child could have been prevented by appropriate intervention during the newborn period.

A mother of a newborn infant said that she thought there was something wrong with her infant's eyes. Examination revealed no defects, but discussion with the mother showed that there was a family history of cataracts and the mother's anxiety was in connection with the possibility that she might have passed these on to her infant through her genes. Had the *origin* of her anxiety about her baby's eyes not been discussed, it would not have been possible to reassure her.

From these illustrations, it becomes apparent that blanket reassurance to parents serves only to blur perceptions and to cut off communications with them about more important matters. While the pediatrician may be very skillful in reassuring parents, he may also, if he overexercises this function, tend to bring about a premature closure of a source of concern in the parents which might better be resolved at this point rather than becoming fixed as a focal point for later difficulties.

4. *In viewing disturbed children, the histories of fears early in childhood often provide crucial clues into the later difficulty even though the early fears may have in themselves been transient and seemingly nonincapacitating for the child.* It seems warranted to be aware, especially during the preschool years, of the occurrence, incidence, and especially increase in numbers of fears. Even the temper tantrums which accompany the stubborn "no" stage of the second year can be a fertile ground for preventive intervention rather than reassurance. To try to understand why the child is afraid and of what he is afraid at this point may be much more valuable than suggesting that all of these fears will go away. The association of such fears with the child striving for independence and the increasing amount of parental control at this period offers a most advantageous field for medical counsel.

5. *Maturation in a psychological sense does not consistently associate itself with physical maturation.* Despite the strong growth tendency in children there are often very great discrepancies in the psychological changes that accompany such physical growth. In addition, psychiatric practice demonstrates strong tendencies

in both children and parents to regress back to earlier "fixation points" where difficulties have been experienced. Whenever such regressions are seen, even though occasionally transitory, they can be signals of difficulty which might be assisted and overcome by proper investigation at that point in time.

Both of these differences in approach to the child grow out of clinical experiences. We hope to demonstrate that such clinical experiences can be shared and that common values in them can be demonstrated. It is futile to think of psychological development in a vacuum. It is, therefore, important that studies of psychological development be tied both to clinical experience and to observations of physical changes. For this reason we have chosen to present our material first in terms of normal development by growth stages and then, subsequently, to describe deviant development in order that pathology can be also understood in a developmental framework.

THE REWARDS OF PRACTICE WITH CHILDREN

Good medical care consists of more than meeting the expectations of patients. The rewards of medical practice lie well beyond the monetary support that society gives the physician. Rather, they are a group of intangibles which are important in themselves. Indeed, the demonstrated monetary rewards of pediatric practice are not in themselves sufficient inducements either for people to go into the field or to remain in it.

Yet, this is not a major dissatisfaction of pediatricians. Rather, such physicians are concerned that they are not able to give as much care to their patient as they would like to do. It has been suggested that long hours are a point of dissatisfaction in pediatrics, but it is apparent that many people in other walks of life, making comparable amounts of money, work equally long hours with perhaps even less satisfaction. It may well be that calling on patients in their homes is more satisfying to pediatricians rather than less, because of the opportunity the pediatrician has to change the disease process more dramatically and quickly than does either the surgeon or the internist.

An important characteristic, however, of pediatricians is a rather strong desire to be liked and also to have warm relations with their patients. It has been demonstrated that the need to help people is extemely strong in the pediatric group, and pediatrics is, in many ways, a most personal discipline in terms of its wish to be of help to people. It is suggested, therefore, that the rewards of any choice of profession must be appropriate to the factors that make one select such a profession.

In this instance, not only is pediatrics a happy choice for many individuals, but the expansion of the discipline to the emotional cares of patients becomes an even more appropriate activity. The gratitude that patients demonstrate if someone listens, attempts to understand, and accepts them as real persons, is both flattering and rewarding.

Pediatrics, however, in its expanded form offers certain special rewards. The rapid and dramatic results of the therapy of acute and infectious diseases occasionally carries over to the early intervention into a psychologic symptom formation. More often, however, the opportunity to identify and resolve early-appearing deviant developmental patterns over a period of time becomes, in itself, the reward. We will attempt to demonstrate later the overwhelming impact of one member of the family on other members of the family. We will attempt to show that the resolution of overdetermined parental concern, be it maternal or paternal, can result in profound changes in the developmental phenomenon of the child. Modification of such concerns by knowledge not only of individual personality development, but of the effect of one parent upon the other is, therefore, important. There is an especial reward in knowing how one promotes such changes.

There is a certain kind of special gratification to the pediatrician in the opportunity of working with younger people whose personalities are not fixed and who can be modified by current knowledge and techniques. The fact that psychologic modification can occur is not always easily demonstrated, but it is important to know that it can be done and that the manifest rewards for parents and children are tremendous.

For those physicians who enjoy working with and meeting with some of their colleagues, adventures into the psychologic aspect of medical practice has a special reward. There are many opportunities for the sharing of such understanding and experience. That in itself has particular meaning for many individuals.

Finally, there is the problem of knowledge. Not only is knowledge a rewarding phenomenon in itself, but it is also one that needs pursuing. To express an interest in the psychologic aspect of growth is one thing: to pursue that interest is another. Mere contact with numbers of children does not provide an increase in knowledge. The experience of practice can be buttressed by understanding. It is our hope that this book will provide interpretations for the physician's already existing observations. Such observations become dramatically useful when it can be seen how they connect with other phases of growth. They also become dramatically rewarding when it becomes possible, through insight, to see how changes occur. It is the purpose of this book to offer both some basic concepts of knowledge about children as well as some insights as to the manner in which growth modifies the individual. The application of both knowledge and insights is necessary to achieve the rewards we suggest.

2

THE PHYSICIAN-PATIENT RELATIONSHIP

THE APPROACH

The crisis that brings any set of parents, concerned about an emotional problem in their child, to pay a visit to the doctor is always real. Every physician knows that behind each such crisis there is nearly always a long history of strained relations between parents and child. From the parent's point of view, however, the critical situation is one that demands prompt attention and, hopefully, some sort of an immediate solution. Such crises are always inopportune in a family's life. They seem to them to be abrupt and demanding of attention. They frequently lead to a confrontation between parents and child that may have been long delayed.

Visualize two parents and their child in the doctor's office. The child has just been expelled from school. The parents, however, have been offered a type of probation if they will seek medical help. The obvious strain of the situation is compelling. Each member of the group is anxious and concerned. The gamut of emotions ranges from fear to a considerable anger. The physician sits in the middle of this tangled skein and feels the various emotions as they surge among the participants. Only with considerable care can the situation be elucidated and some sense made out of the varying emotions (which at this time seem to be primarily passions) that have culminated in this immediate critical situation. Where can the physician begin? It is well initially to take stock of the immediate situation that exists between parents and child, perhaps between parent and parent, and even the involvement that includes the physician himself. Since the parents may well be annoyed at the school's action, they will radiate their anger to all professionals. The physician provides a likely and obvious target. It may be necessary in such a situation to see both parents and child separately in the initial stage. By this means, one can hope to reduce some of the serious external displays of emotion in order to get at the underlying feelings that have led to and are active in precipitating the current situation.

The physician will do well in this instance to permit an immediate and spontaneous type of history rather than to start out with a didactic form of questioning. So involved are the parents in their immediate concerns that a certain amount of ventilation of their anger and resentment is necessary before a more logical kind of history can be taken.

In this first process there will be found many evidences of the strain in the relationships that have existed among these people. Initially, of course, there will be the antagonism against the school for having done something to their child. The fact that the parents, for a long period of time, may have neglected the child or have forced him into a situation which he cannot tolerate will be reacted to in a guilty fashion. This internal guilt will display itself both in the antagonism toward the school and in the displacement of anger to others in the environment. Beaming one's anger at others is an important mechanism designed to protect the parent from his own feelings of guilt and responsibility. In short, parents may try to protect themselves (from the ravages of a cruel but ineffective conscience) by blaming others, including their children, for their own unconsciously felt shortcomings as parents. Such blame is extended to the school, to physicians, and to all who care

MUST THIS CHILD
MAKE THE CHOICE

Fig. 2-1.

for the child as the parent cares for the child. This mechanism has in the past probably motivated much of the parental patterns of discipline. The child is disciplined, usually, with harsh and sudden verbal or physical punishment, not because he needs it but because the parent's unconscious guilt is stirred up by the child's behavior as if such behavior in the child is their own. We see, therefore, in this intricate interaction between parent, child, and those others who care for him, a staging of conflict between the various forces within each of the participants and between each of the participants. The physician is not uninvolved. He is one of the principle characters in the drama and is in a position either to confuse or to enlighten the other participants, depending upon his capacity for skillful observation of himself and others involved and his skillful and resourceful communication.

Such displacement of parental anger and externalization of conflict onto the child and others may come from all sorts of deep-seated personal concerns. These include concerns about being a father or mother, concerns about his or her relation to his own parents, and concerns about the manner in which the child is growing up. Wherever such personal and individual concerns run up against the developing life of the child, there may be outbursts of feeling projected onto the child to cover up for the internal conflicts and points of developmental arrest within the parent.

One's child is, psychologically speaking, a part of one's self. If unacceptable impulses and wishes are so threatening to the parent that they cannot be recognized as even existing within oneself, they cannot be tolerated in one's child. They must be suppressed, repressed, and punished or else denied. This is perhaps what accounts for such inconsistent behavior of parents, at times vacillating between cruel punishment, even beating and damage to the child as, for example, seen in the battered child syndrome, to completely ignoring the child as if to deny that the child exists or is capable of wrong doing. Such vacilation is characteristic of the immature conscience:

A young mother provided clay and paint for her five-year-old son while she herself was painting a difficult assignment in school. When the boy began smearing the paint and clay, she flew into a rage, slapped his face and bit his cheek. She washed his hands and face vigorously in water and soap. Afterwards she felt guilty, ashamed, horrified, and frightened at her actions. She had done to her child what she feared would have been done to her as a child when she made a mess. She had not been able to master successfully the assignment in art and had at that moment experienced the censure of the critical parent internalized as her own conscience. The aggressive attack on her child was like the aggressive attack she feared from her parents as a child. The child was then the bad part of herself which needed to be destroyed in the most primitive way, biting and hitting. This lapse in judgment was temporary. Later when the same child had sleeping difficulties and told her that he was afraid that another child would hit him, she had learned sufficiently about her own difficulties to be able to reassure the child by telling him that she knew he was upset about her having hit him and that she was sorry that she had lost her temper and would try not to do so again. The child was much reassured and was able to overcome the sleeping difficulty.

The fact that parents, themselves, may have been very closely involved with the difficulties which the child has had over the years is met by a still other mechanism of defense, namely isolation:

A father, in such a situation, was indignant because the child had been expelled from school for beating up other children on the playground. The father could not understand this behavior in his son because, as he pointed out, the child was exemplary in his behavior at home, never got into fights with his siblings, and was in all ways a perfect gentleman. Later on in the history he described the intensity of punishment which he meted out to this son for any minor infraction of family regulations. Yet it was impossible for him to see that the son was meting out the same sort of punishment to his fellows. The absolute isolation of one series of events from the other served to shield him from anxiety and guilt regarding his own behavior. Thus, the extraordinarily efficient mechanism of isolation serves as a protective device to keep one free from confronting reactions in oneself which are grossly obvious to others.

THE HISTORY

At this point the physician may begin to take an historical look at the family situation. This may be done by proceeding backwards through the school years and discussing the preschool preparations of the child and then his early childhood and infancy. Or he may choose, having gathered an adequate history of the present difficulty and having seen the various mechanisms that the parents are using at the present time, to go back to the very beginning and start forward. In so doing, certain essentials of the relationship are of crucial importance.

In the history of the pregnancy the physician will not only be looking for evidence of various parturient pathologies, but also for evidence of emotional distress on the part of the mother. This may be manifest directly in terms of her own concerns, fears, worries, and anxieties or may be expressed indirectly in terms of discomfort throughout the period. The symptoms of nausea, vomiting, or a great sense of the child being a burden to her warrant specific questions. A careful and detailed history of the birth itself is necessary to verify or eliminate evidence of fetal distress.

When present, this may be a forerunner of an organic involvement which frequently underlies behavioral disorders.

It is critically important to try to establish a picture of the newborn as the mother saw him. This is not always easy to do. Parental memories are often inadequate, and many of the relationships have been uncomfortable enough to be denied and covered up in the process of time. However, many mothers can remember difficulties in their care of the child when they cannot recall their own sensations of worry or antagonism. Mothers will describe aberrations in feeding or sleeping (such as will be discussed in the later chapters). It is well to catalogue these early difficulties with care because of their historical significance. Evidence suggests that the establishment of a good or bad relationship with the child may well be made at this point. In listening to the mother talk of this period it is well to keep in mind the fact that what she says, like a ballad, consists of both words and music. The major message may be in how she talks about this period, rather than in what she says; in what she doesn't say, rather than in what she does say.

The same is true of the subsequent history. In nearly every case, it will be possible to trace difficulties gradually taking form throughout the early years of the child's life. The early history should look for somatic disturbances and later on for behavioral and control difficulties. Particularly with the advent of the second year, one begins to ask about the kind of troubles that beset some families where the control of the child's growing independence is a major factor. This may be elicited by tracing the history of various learning processes: the manner in which the child learns to speak or the manner in which the child gains prowess in his motor behavior. In addition, there are certain crucial learning experiences: that around feeding oneself, and that concerned with the toilet-training process. Parents may at this point offer comments about certain aspects of behavior such as an excess of temper tantrums or a seeming great need for punishment.

As one proceeds in the history, he may find difficulties during the preschool years when parents are concerned about the child's

Fig. 2-2. Father may also be skilled as parent.

sexual curiosity. Equally, they may be worried about his dreams, his nightmares, or other fantasies. The manner in which children observe other children, their need to explore, and their curiosity about sex often comprise troubles for certain families and they should be inquired into. When one comes to the history of the school-age child, certain areas which will be considered in detail later require special consideration. It is important to get the parent to describe the separation process at the time that the child goes to school. Grades and comments of teachers are often good indices of the child's general behavior. The parents can equally describe the prowess and contact with his peers as well as his activities at home and in sports. In talking about adolescence, it is important for the parent to describe the changes that occur as the child goes through early puberty, both in growth and in emotional characteristics. A detailed consideration of adolescence will be found in the chapter pertinent to this; and since it is at the end of the line in child psychiatry, historical material is nearly always present material.

In all of this history taking, certain things are of greater importance. It has been shown, for example, that the number of complaints that a parent makes about the child indicates not only the extent of pathology in the child but also the extent of the parent's involvement in the pathological process. Where the parents can be seen together, it is extremely important to get a current picture of the personalities of these two parents as well as their different views about the child-rearing process and the development of symptomatology in the child. It is often possible to get one parent to describe the personality of the other, knowing that the other will have his chance in a few moments. Such descriptions bring out very clearly opposing points of view as well as some idea of the type of personality of the parent which would, in many ways, relate to the pathology in the child.

Recently, we saw a parent who gave a long and involved history of the difficulties which her son was undergoing. When asked to describe her husband, she, in essence, related exactly the same story. It was a great surprise to her to see the two compared, for she had herself never made any comparison between her husband and her son. It was apparent, however, that the father was encouraging pathology in his boy: a pathology which was identical with that of himself.

THE CHILD

Having obtained such a history, the physician will do well to see the child quite independently of the parents whenever this is possible. If it is a child that one knows, it is equally important to try to separate this particular observation of the child from the history taking and formal office contact that has preceded. The interview with the child in trying to unravel a psychologic situation varies with the physician's knowledge of the child and the child's age. It is impressive how many children can be comfortably interviewed in an office situation without the use of gadgets or gimmicks if they are considered to be people in their own right and allowed to talk.

It is most useful initially to establish a level of interested concern through the use of some piece of history which the child can see as pertinent. For most school-age children, an opening comment about school, whether or not this is the presenting problem, often establishes a level on which the child can talk about himself and his own concerns without being bothered by the behavioral difficulties that have brought him to the physician. For example, the physician may do well to discuss the child's general progress in school in order to bring out those areas in which he is most competent and perhaps those with which he has difficulty. Then one can switch over to the peer situation in terms of other children in the school setting. From there it is usually easy to lead to a discussion of the child's home and neighborhood activities and finally to get to the home situation. Equally, it is often simpler to get children to talk about their home situation in terms of siblings, house arrangements, meals, and all of the other activities of daily life, rather than to talk directly about emotional relationships between themselves and their parents. A child who talks freely about his dislike of a sibling may show great hesitancy in talking about a real concern relative to his mother or father. The natural guilt that children have over their bad feelings toward their parents may, in many ways, inhibit their talking about those things which may be uppermost on their mind.

Such an approach applies as well to more extended contacts with children. Fortunate, indeed, is the physician who has established a relationship with a child over a period of time. In considering prevention, it is most advantageous if the normal ongoing contacts of the physician with the child include some discussion of the child's life outside the office. This avoids the awkwardness that arises when a critical situation occurs. At such a time the physician, even knowing a child, finds he must make an abrupt transition from previous medical office activities to the child's life outside. If, in handling such a patient over a period of time, the physician has from time to time asked about home, school, peers, and so forth, he will find himself in a greatly advantageous situation when it comes time to discuss a behavioral crisis.

TALKING WITH THE SICK CHILD

Certain definite changes take place in the child's emotional life when he is ill. Some of these very much affect the attitude of the physician to the child, as well as the manner in which rapport can be established with the child. One important change is that a very dependent relationship is established by the fact of the child being ill. This is true whether he is sick at home or in a hospital. While it is true that a child being seen in a pediatric office is dependent upon the physician to set the tone for contacts, interview, conversation, and so on, this dependency is much more obvious when the child is bedridden and finds himself lying down with someone looking at him. Furthermore, the same kind of regression that occurs in us adults when we become sick may be exaggerated in the child. The response of a child to the physician, therefore, is compounded both of dependence and of regression to earlier behavioral patterns.

Second, the impact of the illness alters our feeling about the behavioral process in the child. In general, we are very concerned about what is happening to the child, and our interests, skill, and attention are focused on making the child well. We find ourselves so involved with those activities that surround his care (as well as the attention which the parents demand of us) that it is not easy to continue to discuss with the child his other ongoing activities. Yet, it is obvious from numerous case situations that the rapport which is built up with the child during the illness consists of more than a discussion of his immediate disease. The child-patient is extremely grateful for the physician who will talk to him not only about his aches and pains but about those experiences and activities which he has had to abandon. In fact, many of the child's questions will concern how soon he is going to play ball, go back to school, or meet with his friends. It is important, therefore, not to forget that the intercurrent illness is only a part of the total life activity of the child.

Because of mistakes made in the past, we have all been overly cautioned about not doing those things which will frighten the child as we discuss his illness. Almost all children think about or attempt to figure out the nature of their illness, or, if some medical or surgical procedure is planned, attempt to anticipate what is going to take place. These thoughts are the child's way of attempting to master a stressful situation as his own bodily integrity is threatened. Because the child lacks real knowledge and experience, his own explanations of his illness or the anticipated procedure often reflect a strange mixture of fantasy and reality colored by current concerns in his life situation. Children often believe that they have become ill or have gotten injured because they were bad and must be punished. One child in the family is often jealous of another child who, because of illness, receives more attention, care, special food, than the well child. These special things are equated with love which the parent gives to one but not to the other. Children sometimes hold themselves responsible for illness or death of someone else in the family, particularly someone toward whom they have been jealous or competitive. Some examples of children's misconceptions follow:

A six-year-old boy had a hairy mole removed from his left anterior thigh under general anesthesia. When he awakened and returned to the pediatric ward, he asked his pediatrician where his "little mole" was, explaining that he had expected to take care of it after it was cut off.

An eight-year-old girl with asthma had been given Epicac when the asthmatic attacks were particularly severe. Since she often vomited after being given Epicac, she concluded that asthma was an illness which caused "your insides to fill up with poison stuff and when you got rid of all the poison then you could breath better again."

A twelve-year-old boy entered surgery with the understanding that he would have an operation to bring an undescended testicle down to the scrotum. The testicle was found to be atrophic, was removed, and a herniorraphy was done. This was explained to the boy afterwards. Two years later the boy developed nightmares, did poorly in school, was afraid of heights, and frightened of being alone in the dark. One of the boy's central fantasies was the thought that he had had two testicles before the operation and that he had had two operations, one on each testicle. He believed that he would not be able to produce a baby because it took two things to make a baby and one of his was gone. After many more references to the operation and many more fantasies about the anesthesia, the experience of being told about two operations, and so forth, much of his symptomatology decreased and he became less anxious about growing up.

Talking with the children and families about illness, operations, and being in the hospital provides two important safeguards to the child's mental health. First, it provides an opportunity for the child to master a complicated stressful situation through conscious thought as reflected in spoken words. Secondly, it provides an opportunity to the child to clarify the differences between fantasy and reality. It is often the most trivial medical detail of an illness, operation, or medical procedure which becomes the focus of a particular misunderstanding. In order to prevent emotional ills arising out of physical ones, one must be ready to listen attentively to the child and help him feel comfortable in coming to his own focus of concern, never assuming that the focus of medical concern coincides with that of the child. In our talking with children we are ever sensitive to the fact that they are vulnerable to the anxiety of adults and we may at times withdraw from communication with the child rather than take the chance of stirring up any unnecessary anxiety. This is usually a mistake but, as in most things in life, a careful balance of positive and negative factors involved must be considered.

The extreme of this situation is seen in the child in whom we have already made a clinical impression that the disease is potentially lethal or even terminal. At such times we tend very quickly to abandon the child and focus our acute clinical activities on the illness itself. This is entirely appropriate to the situation and yet, in any prolonged illness the child becomes panicked, not by the effects of the disease but by the lack of communication. Observations of children ill with such diseases suggest that the same kind of process applies in other and less serious intercurrent diseases. Whenever we get focused too intently on the disease process, we forget the individual who bears this illness, and children, perhaps more than adults, are particularly susceptible to being ignored, often equating this with being abandoned. Most children are unconcerned about the disease process except as it causes them bodily discomfort, but they are very concerned about their general life activities, even though for the time being these may be rather limited by bed, television screen, books, and so on. The physician who utilizes this opportunity not only for observation of the child, but for an opportunity to talk to him about the most mundane things, succeeds in establishing a rapport which may pay very valuable preventive rewards later on. In times like this a discussion of totally nongermane matters may make the difference between a good subsequent rapport and a feeling of distrust on the part of the patient.

CONTACT WITH THE WHOLE FAMILY

Something should be mentioned about the use of the entire family as patients. Not only in psychologic investigation but in current approaches to therapy, the entire family is being seen in order to try to understand the conflict that has arisen. In many ways there are tremendous assets to this situation. Since interpersonal difficulties, which we will subsequently describe, arise in families, it is not surprising that they can be demonstrated when a whole family group is seen together. Indeed, the critical situation that brings patients to physicians is often made dramatically more clear by having all members of the family present and talking about it.

Certain hazards accompany this diagnostic process, however. One is the cultural reluctance on the part of parents and children to talk freely to one another. Families who will quarrel continuously at home over some matter find themselves unable to bring out these antagonistic feelings with the physician. In addition, there are cultural mores which determine what one says in front of somebody else, particularly on the part of children. The unfortunate aspect of such family confrontation is that the parents use the physician to act as a sounding board for their emotions and yet, both openly and silently, deny the child the opportunity to speak. It is all too easy for the physician to become directly involved as a participant in the family conflict. In addition, in such instances, the physician finds himself being used as a tool to carry out a punishing act that the parent considers appropriate. There is a great danger in allowing oneself to be used in this way. It is because of this that we suggested earlier that in most situations interviews with parents and child be conducted separately.

When the physician takes the opportunity to sit between parents and child in such a family conference, be it for diagnosis or for subsequent help, he must remember that he is responsible to each member of the family to hear, to understand, and to interpret to the others. The mere mechanical arrangements and problems in communication in such a setting are tremendous, aside from the problem of understanding the complex issues. Considerable skill and training is needed before getting involved in such a situation. On the other hand, the physician who is acquainted with the family may find that he has great advantage in sitting down with all of them rather than separately, in order that he may see for himself with his own eyes certain things that they have erroneously been reporting to him in their individual sessions.

THE PHYSICIAN'S EXPECTATIONS

Various studies have focused from time to time upon the "ideal" patient. Unfortunately, these studies bring out the fact that the ideal patient is often not a very interesting individual. Both physicians in training and physicians in practice frequently tend to see the ideal patient as a subservient, dependent, ingratiating type of individual. Such individuals are thought to be ideal because they give their story freely, listen carefully to the doctor's instructions, and follow them out completely. More than their dependence, these patients need to please the physician. The physician may then become pleased with the patient. While patient and physician may become pleased with each other, this does not carry any assurance of the patient being helped or of the physician learning much about the patient. Such patients offer very little stimulation to the physician, and, unfortunately, even in their passive dependency, they are not necessarily conscientious in carrying out medical instructions. Over a period of time the physician and patient become disillusioned with each other, much as lovers who have nothing in common except each other as a source of admiration.

Particularly in the area of the behavioral disorders of both adults and children, such parents are seen only rarely. The type of patient we are more often apt to encounter is the patient who makes considerable demands, the patient who has a series of complaints that are not easily avoided, and the patient who expects a response on the part of the physician without necessarily feeling that thanks for compliance has to be offered. Thus, we are not usually dealing with a readily accepting type of patient. We must gear our procedures and understandings not only to meet the described aberrations of the child, but also to be able to take a history and to try to understand individuals who themselves are often upsetting to us as physicians. Here it is that not only our knowledge of growth, change, and personality development come into play, but also our own attributes of being able to tolerate both the anxiety of the patient and the antagonism that the patient exhibits against all who review and question, rather than agree and gratify.

Other observations suggest that our picture of the ideal patient is somewhat akin to our own professional selves. We tend to grow impatient with patients who are poor observers or whom we suspect of distorting of the facts of an illness. This is particularly noticeable in history taking. We may ask the parent about the times of onset of certain developmental stages. The answer may very well be, "Oh, he's just like all children," or "Why, he's quite normal." Such answers are not only unsatisfying to us in terms of the specific observations that we are seeking, but they may annoy us because they seem to be evasions of a crucial area of our history-taking process. When one begins to see an abundance of such answers, one may suspect that the parent is very anxious, a poor observer, attempting to conceal certain definite areas of the child's development, or that the parent is as yet unable to trust the physician. It is possible for the physician to accept the forgetting of certain details of a child's development, especially if the child is in the late school period or in adolescence. On the other hand, we may see the behavior of parents who describe their child "like any child" or "normal," as defensive avoidance or having to come to terms with long-standing problems in their relationship with their child.

It is well, in such instances, to sort out our annoyance, based on our expectations of good observations, from our scientific concern, which will permit us to get at the same factual material by proceeding in another direction. We should be aware that not only are the parents unwilling to look at the defects in their child, but they are entitled to a certain amount of pride in their children and, therefore, may make conscious efforts to avoid describing defects.

Equally confusing to us in our expectations are parents who tend to exaggerate the prowess of their child. Rather than be annoyed with the parent for making his child better than he seems to be or to challenge these claims directly, it is well to remember such exaggerations, to be compared at a later date against objective findings: be they neighborhood reports, school notations, or the specific comments of other physicians who have seen the child and parents.

Earlier we discussed the mechanisms of displacement, projection, and rationalization as attempts to cover up the parents' real concern about an activity, an emotional display, or a failure in emotional development. The obviousness of such mechanisms often leads to annoyance on the part of the physician. This is especially true of those displacements of hostility towards the child or projections of blame toward society which are redirected to helpful professionals and particularly against the physician himself. It is not easy to be met with the hostility of patients. Even when we are fully aware that it is not our due, it is hard for us to avoid becoming embroiled in it. Most commonly we are tempted to a counter-reaction in an effort to defend ourselves and have the parent more properly appraise us. Needless to say, if we succumb to such defensive maneuvers ourselves, we have little chance of seeing our patients drop their defensive armor.

We have also commented on this matter when we discussed the

fact that as physicians concerned with children, we are quite likely to become allies to the child with the parent as an opponent. Although this is one of the most obvious traps in medical practice relating to children, it nonetheless is a very prevalent one. We must continually take stock of our own inner responses to parents in order that we not spend our time fighting with them. Rather, we should try to allay their fears, understand their guilt reactions, and, hopefully, modify their actions, attitudes, and behaviors towards the child whom we think we are protecting. A saying popular earlier in this century was that there are "no bad children, only bad parents." To practice the psychologic aspects of pediatric care with this in mind is tantamount to failure. If parents have defects that we can discern in the history-taking process, it is better to think in terms of treatment than of punishment. The mere fact that we are annoyed at the method used by the parent in handling the child gives us no permission to be lawyer, judge, policeman, or other punitive officer. Our expectations of parents strongly test our capacity to be physicians.

PARENTAL EXPECTATIONS

If we have such expectations of our patients, what about the parents' expectations of us as physicians? This relationship may be viewed on many levels. As with any social encounter, there are certain conscious expectations on both sides. However, these are often not expressed, each assuming what the other has in mind. Let us take a case example:

Mrs. R. brought Mark, age ten months, for well-baby care, indicated that the major problem was the fact that he was always crying and rubbing his gums. His sleep was restless; he chewed on everything in reach. The pediatrician pointed out he was teething. The mother said, "Yes, I know. Can you give me something to put on his gums to make him more comfortable?"

Comment. This encounter is a classic example of one of the most basic assumptions the parent has about the pediatrician. This parent expects the pediatrician not only to help her understand this immediate crisis but her urgent expectation is for relief for herself and for her child. In this case, she assumes that this relief must come in terms of doing something for the child rather than something directly to her. The doctor, however, is in a difficult spot. It is true that his whole training has prepared him to relieve suffering, and he gains in his feelings of professional integrity when he can do so. He knows, however, from his experience, that the anxiety the mother is having about this teething cannot be fully treated by medication applied to the gums. The fact that there is a long list of remedies available for this is a confirmation that the universal panacea has not been found. The assumption, however, on the part of the parent that the pediatrician can relieve the tension in the gums is so strong that the pedatrician can assume that his major function is to relieve this tension. Therefore, he is left with the only recourse; that is, to do what the mother suggests or try one of his own favorite solutions. At least he gives temporary relief in the form of some activity for the mother, and, hopefully, the activity of putting on a medication will help her reduce her tension. His topical application relieves her immediate sense of concern but does not necessarily solve the problem of her anxiety about the growing child.

Other assumptions that parents have about their children are somewhat less easily recognized. A very important one is the relief of guilt. There is often an expectation on the part of a parent that by treatment, he or she will be relieved of a responsibility for the child's distress. This is a reasonable expectation because it is understood that the pediatrician understands children. He is an authority on what causes their distress and, therefore, ought to be able to relieve the concern the parent feels about his or her own role in creating the distress. Many of the reassurances which we dispense daily are calculated to reduce unconscious guilt feelings in parents. We can, quite honestly, promise a parent that nothing he or she has done has led to the onset of measles, but we are not so clear when we come to talking about a child who has an accident in his second year. Yet, we frequently strive to reduce this guilt because the parents expect it of us. This will be discussed in much greater detail later on because it becomes a very important factor in the onset of neurotic disturbances in children.

Next, the parent wishes to have her ideas about what causes disturbances acknowledged and confirmed by the pediatrician. The psychologists have labeled this phenomenon "consensual validation." If there is agreement as to what has caused the difficulty, it increases the parent's sense of competence and enables her to meet the difficulty adaptively. Unfortunately, the questioning attitude of the parent provides a testing ground for the pediatrician, especially when the parent knows an answer prior to offering a question to the physician.

An outstanding example was seen in an emergency room where a young resident was met by a family of gypsies who sought help because of an older child who had been coughing. On examination of the child, the pediatrician discovered dextrocardia. The parents and elders looked on with interest as the chest was examined and when the pediatrician announced that the heartbeat was louder on the right side than the left, they all smiled in agreement for they all knew the diagnosis. They then introduced a second child who was suffering from vomiting and diarrhea and obviously acutely ill.

Comment. Before they could trust the doctor with the sick child, they had to test him to see whether or not he was a good physician. Having passed this test and having consensually validated their findings, he could now be trusted with the sick member. The red herrings which patients throw out to us provide a way the parent can get to know about the physician before they trust him with the care of their child.

Another basic, but often unexpressed, assumption is that the pediatrician to whom the parent takes her child will consider the child to be of prime importance. This importance will be demonstrated by the manner in which the physician becomes interested in the child. Parents particularly note the way their distress as well as the child's illness is recognized and recorded, both in the memory of the doctor and on the medical chart. The pediatrician who forgets the child's name or whether a child is a boy or a girl demonstrates to the parent a lack of meeting this particular expectation. Physicians over the years have always been bothered by patients who wish to check the chart or read what the doctor has written. This is not merely morbid curiosity, nor is it a desire purely to understand what is the matter with the patient. Rather, it is to make sure that the physician is uniquely interested in this specific patient and has taken every pain to understand with whom he is dealing.

Certain bizarre assumptions come into pediatric practice as well as into the general practice of medicine. There are patients who feel that talking about the symptoms of their child gives them and the child a certain status. If the symptom has a definite name and syndrome, it establishes a sense of dignity for the child and the parent. Thus, it becomes a socially dictated expectation among certain people that they take their troubles to a physician. They would be uncomfortable if the child had problems which were known to the child's peers or neighbors which had not been discussed with the physician.

It may seem strange that in this list of assumptions, actual understanding of the disease has not been mentioned. It is curious that many parents, particularly those presenting behavioral symptoms, seem to have more concern about superficial assumptions in their relationship to the doctor than they do about that of actually understanding the cause. While many parents are quick to point out that "nobody understands me," they are not necessarily saying that the illness of my child is misunderstood. Rather, they are saying that nobody understands them at the level where they would like to be understood. They have their own concepts of the illness, as we have noticed, and they prefer a diagnosis and understanding that matches what they wish, rather than that which the clinical judgment of the physician may prescribe.

Out of these assumptions the pediatrician may usually form stereotyped notions of parents' expectations. It becomes simple to classify parents as "this overanxious mother," "this rejecting mother," "this status-conscious suburban young matron," "this tense person." The stereotypes which all of us build stand in the way of our actual judgment of our patients. We need to ask further,

"Overanxious about what, rejecting of what, status-conscious of what, tense in what way?" The stereotypes are built out of assumptions about patients and their manner of presenting themselves to us, including their assumptions of what we should do for them. The value of these stereotypes, however, is extremely limited. Furthermore, stereotypes always interfere with a true clinical knowledge of the situation between parent and child as well as between parent and physician. If we are concerned about their expectations of us, it is well not to have a false set of expectations about them. To stereotype a patient often leads a patient to stereotype his expectations of the physician. This leads to a stalemate in the development of the physician-patient relationship.

PART II

NORMAL DEVELOPMENT

3

INTRODUCTION TO NORMAL DEVELOPMENT

The present century has been described as the century of the child. Obviously, this is not because children are in themselves different from what they have been for eons past. During the past sixty years, however, adults have paid more attention to them, have looked at their progress, and have begun to conceptualize the importance of the growth process. In constructing a preventive approach to the emotional problems of children, it is necessary to utilize all of this knowledge from two major points of view—that of the child and that of the parent. The material to be presented in this book attempts to utilize the knowledge of growth and development in an overall fashion which considers both the multiple phases of growth in the child and the intricate responses of the parent to this growth process. It will become apparent that there is a growth process in parents that must, in some fashion, correspond to the growth process in children in order that the best results be produced.

Growth in the child must be seen in the light of a variety of patterns. Not only does the child grow in physical strength and stature, but intellectual, emotional, and social growth patterns can also be described and must be related. The fact that there is a homogeneous pattern of character and appearance building up in the child is a result of a variety of separate growth patterns that are occurring both independently and in concert. While development is never a smooth and easy process, there is an incremental aspect that is of extreme importance. What happens to the child

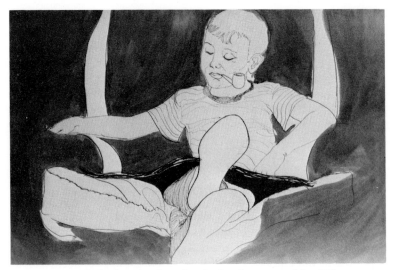

Fig. 3-1. This has often been described as the century of the child.

during any one phase of growth leaves a residue on which the rest of growth must be built. Deviation and handicaps at any one time leave an impact on the child that modifies future steps and stages of the whole growth activity. Therefore, it is important to be concerned not only with the quantitative phenomenon of growth but with the rate, sequence, and timing of a whole host of events that culminate in the character, personality, structure, and appearance of the child.

The ground plan on which this building occurs is formed by a combination of the results of heredity and those phases of growth that take place in utero. Certain basic patterns of behavior can be seen in every child at the moment of birth. These are highly individual but quickly begin to reflect the impact of the outside world. Thus, we see manifest in the very small infant a pattern of general behavior which will become modified either toward health or toward pathology in all areas of the child's being. The development of the normal personality is constantly accompanied by the possibilities of psychopathology, but there are also wide individual variations in growth which are not in themselves abnormal.

It is important, therefore, to understand the normal patterns of growth, development, and emotional progress in order to understand the developmental pathology or psychopathology which may accompany such growth. The principle of such development includes the satisfaction of definite stages of growth in order that other stages may be successfully accomplished. The child is faced, as Erikson points out, by a series of crises of development, each of which needs handling in its own fashion and at its own time.

The early interaction of the child and its environment provides a further base for the development of social and emotional responses. No child grows in a vacuum, and the child's growth prospers not only by the satisfaction of simple needs, such as hunger, but also by the satisfaction of social needs. These are met by a variety of stimulating activities. They may be as simple as the smile of the mother or as complex as the learning which is offered in the process of reading. At any rate, such interaction also builds on earlier interactions, and each phase of development depends on a successful culmination of an earlier relationship between the child and the stimulating or depriving environment in which he lives.

To understand the parental role in this whole process, one must consider the attitudinal modifications that the parent must make in fostering the various stages of the life of the child. In addition, there are internal forces which rise up within a parent and affect his consideration of his own child. Observations of normal development suggest certain aspects of care which are inherent in human relations. The parent feeds, clothes, teaches, limits, and disciplines his child. The proper combination of all of these activities leads to the best development and the best growth of the child, but all of us bring to the rearing of children some concerns and anxieties, either about our own growth or about the manner in which we were handled by our parents and others. These anxieties demonstrate themselves in the form of fear, anger, shame, or guilt. They make a profound impression on the child— as deep an impression as is made by love. The child seems equally sensitive to positive and to negative feelings.

These anxieties are crucially important in understanding the development of the child, as well as the development of pathological personality patterns. Such parental reactions have to be seen in a timing and sequence that is complementary to the timing and sequence of the development of the child. In certain instances, the anxieties of parents are pervasive and accompany the whole of the child's development. In other instances, as we shall point out, parents are comfortable in handling children at some age periods and very uncomfortable in handling children at other times. Some parents cling to their children and to the babyhood of their children. Others are anxious that the child rush through childhood in order to attain the independent activity of the older child or adult.

All of these modifications of the approach to the child affect the normal progress of growth and development. Conflicts between parents also reflect themselves in a manner in which the child is handled and cared for so that conflictual settings within a family, either parent-parent, parent-child, or parent-child-child, may lead to modifications that are extremely important to the observer of development.

In order to demonstrate the intricate interactions of all of these activities, we have chosen to present our clinical material in two major sections. This portion concerns the normal development of the child and the parental response which accompanies it. The second clinical part will be concerned with the pathology that is demonstrated by children as they grow and the relationship of such pathology to the fact of growth itself. The role of the parent, both in helping the child to grow and in participating in abnormality, will be stressed. We have already made the premise that assistance to parents needs to be based on a knowledge of development. It is hoped that such knowledge can lead to both anticipation and prevention.

4

THE FIRST YEAR

To understand the newborn's impact on those who take care of him, it is first necessary to consider his native equipment, both physical and psychological. It is not sufficient to say that he is a voracious mass of protoplasm, although this comment suggests both the diffuseness of the infant's psychophysiological organization as well as the demands he makes on the world. In addition to manifesting such imperative needs as food and water, it becomes quickly apparent that the newborn begins very early the process of organization of his primitive reflex patterns, his instinctual demands, and his sensory equipment for coping with the world.

As will be noted later, the infant presents himself to the mother as a highly sentimentalized human being. She is greatly concerned that he be whole and intact and free of illness. She is also concerned as to the sex of her baby, and we will discuss later the importance of her discovery of this particular item. But even this diffusely organized individual is capable of a certain number of organized responses and capable of quickly learning ways of approaching the caretaker.

INITIAL BEHAVIOR PATTERNS

We are well acquainted with the response of rooting by which the child's mouth finds the nipple and then becomes linked to the sucking response. In a healthy newborn the ability to suck is demonstrated relatively quickly, although certain components of the sucking act, such as the use of the tongue, require time for their organization and the building up a competent reflex pattern. The infant has the capacity to be uncomfortable when his needs are not met or when he is presented with distinctively painful situations. This part of the organization of the child's existence, centering around phenomena of pain and pleasure, very quickly begins to be demonstrated.

There is every evidence that certain physical needs, of which hunger seems to be outstanding, become manifest very quickly by a generalized pattern of discharge which spreads itself throughout the body. Waking quietly from a sleep, the child begins to whimper and to cry more and more loudly until his total behavior demonstrates body discomfort marked by muscular activity involving most of the skeletal system.

Studies of older infants have suggested the great importance of a *variety* of caretaking procedures. Most of these are met by the ordinary handling that the mother offers, not only in the hygienic care of the child, but in her fondling, petting, and other associated actions. Many of these activities serve to protect the child from the outside world, as well as from his inner sources of tension. In the neonatal period, however, when the infant is hungry, the need for food transcends other matters of care. It is important to observe the impact of such nutrient care on the child. A healthy, hungry baby, utilizing the maximum of his reflex ability, quickly learns to locate the breast, attaches himself to it, and through sucking satisfies his current needs. When these needs are satisfied, one senses not only a sense of comfort in the infant, but also the relaxation of all of the highly charged diffuse muscle patterns. Sleep usually intervenes, and the infant is comfortable once more until there is recurrence of physiologic hunger. Thus, we observe an extremely important and fundamental cycle of discomfort, followed by tension, followed by external action, and then succeeded by relaxation. This pattern, shown at first in relation to hunger and being fed, becomes, as time goes on, a form of response of the infant to social situations. It is the fact that the mother satisfies these particular tension demands that leads to the establishment of the infant's prime bond with the caring mother and sets the pattern for all that happens with others who follow.

INITIAL SENSORY PATTERNS

It has been assumed that just as most behavioral patterns (except for the reflexes) of the infant tend to be diffuse in nature, the sensory equipment of the infant is equally diffuse, not developed, and nonspecific. Certain studies, however, are beginning to suggest that the organization of the infant's sensory patterns, begun prior to birth, begins to expand rapidly soon after birth. It has been demonstrated, for example, that infants are more sensitive to higher tones, although it is not clear what relation this has to the higher pitched voice of the mother. It has been shown that the infant can very early anticipate the feeding by a series of subtle sensory cues and that the newborn can utilize central vision and use both eyes in a coordinated fashion. It is equally apparent that the infant's sensory response is a highly variable thing from child to child. While it has been possible currently to describe children as hypertonic, normotonic, and relaxed, we are only beginning to appreciate the extremely important visceral responses that accompany these evidences of outward motor behavior. There tends to be a pattern of visceral behavior which is consistent for any one child and which sets a demand on the part of the parent and on those who advise parents in understanding the level of function of any one child. The responses of individual children follow relatively similar patterns, but, as might be expected, the child with a highly charged visceral system starts from the higher base-line in terms of his response. Richmond and others have well demonstrated this in terms of the pulse rate, respirations, and skin reactions.

An extremely important sensory modality in the contact between caretaker and child is demonstrated in the kinesthetic system. The response of the child to different handling has been apparent for centuries. We are only beginning to be able to measure the extent of this response and of the conditions which promote it. Clinically, it has been suggested that tension in some form is communicated from the handler to the infant, but it has not been clear as to the manner through which this tension, or lack of it, has been conveyed. We are accustomed to seeing two different individuals pick up a baby and find that one is able to soothe by appropriate handling and another stimulate it to further discomfort. Additionally, we are aware that a variety of factors attendant upon the nursing process make for the comfort of a baby over and above the mere intake of food. The suckling process, which has value in itself, is nearly always accompanied by maternal handling—fondling, petting, soothing—and by the speech of the mother as well. In a healthy situation there is a quick response to this handling process, a response which begins to modify the tension of discomfort even prior to the intake of food. It seems apparent that a child must have kinesthetic responses mediated through a variety of receptors that make it possible for these stimuli to be effective. It appears that the organization of the infant contains elements fully capable of responding through a generalized visceral and somatic relaxation to the ministrations and handling of the parent. The full impact of the importance of this upon the infant can be seen in studies of older infants who have been deprived of such handling. This will be discussed subsequently. More important, in the infantile period such handling sets a pattern of behavior not only for the actions and activity of the child but for the reactions and relationships of the child with the most prominent caretaker—usually the mother.

MENTAL AND PHYSICAL DEVELOPMENT

Earlier we used the word "voracious" in describing the character of the newborn. Observations of a small baby suggest that, regardless of the child's capacity to appreciate himself, his demands are those of omnipotence. There is no hesitation on the part of the child in making his wants known. Initially, there is no apparent clue from the child that suggests there is anyone else to be cared for at the time. Thus, the child is highly selfish and highly self-centered. The insatiability of his demands suggests that he recognizes the outer world only in terms of what it has to give to him. While this primordial selfishness is normally modified by growth, all of us manifest some clinging to this auspicious period in our lives when our demands were instantly and comfortably met. It is easy to see that the manner in which the infant's demands are met is a powerful force in modifying the initial narcissistic behavior that is so clearly demonstrated.

As the infant develops the ability to gain satisfaction and security from the sucking process, and as the nurture of feeding gives rise to bodily growth and development, the possibilities for subsequent motor and mental development begin to demonstrate themselves. Following the general law of cephalocaudal development, the child begins to demonstrate the ability to hold the head, to use the eyes, to manipulate the face, to gradually organize the back and arms, and eventually the lower trunk and legs. Throughout this motor progress there is an attendant social progress which is made possible by the fact that the child's horizon changes, enlarges, and becomes more organized. Here one sees the very complex interplay of motor development and behavior. Each mother is extremely pleased with every evidence of healthy and normal development. She works hard to elicit a smile as the reward for the effort she has poured into care and stimulation of her baby. When she is thus rewarded the child develops a concomitant social response and a proportionate social reward. Thus, the impact of parental stimulation, along with neurologic organization, becomes clearly seen.

The sensory modalities of sight, hearing, touch, and feel become progressively organized during the first year, and all contribute to the behavioral pattern of the infant and his response to the social environment. The increasing capacities first to see, then to fixate, then to organize a picture, and then to respond make an outstanding example of the organizational capacity of the infant and the extreme importance of a social response that involves the infant's capacity to change. Progressively, the child's skeletal capacity to sit (as opposed to lying) not only widens his horizon, but changes his ability to respond to the adult's image of the environment, and to give back once more some of the parental behavioral cues. Certain general physiologic patterns become well established during this year. As the child's appetite is satisfied, it becomes quickly apparent that the child is able to tolerate periods of hunger longer, as well as to take in amounts which will suffice to establish a physiologic nutrient for a longer period of time. Thus, the feeding schedule becomes lengthened and gradually merges into the classical three-meal-a-day pattern of our particular society. Equally, changes take place in the sleeping pattern, usually quite early. The sleeping needs of the infant diminish as time goes on so that the almost continuous sleep of the small infant becomes spaced out into one long period of nighttime sleep and daytime naps. Certain infants find major difficulty in adjusting to the conventional day-night schedules, a fact partly related to the cultural phenomenon which can be seen in disorganized homes, but also probably related to certain fundamental situations within the infant himself. This will be discussed in Chap. 17.

The outstanding phenomenon of disturbed sleep in the latter part of the first year is a clinical experience that is common to many children and becomes pathological in only a few. It is important here to stress the normalcy of this particular phenomenon. Many a child who has established a good sleep pattern and who goes quickly to sleep after his evening meal during the second, third, or fourth month of life, develops an annoying pattern of startle and subsequent wakefulness between the seventh and ninth month. This period of wakefulness tends to occur late in the evening and is characterized by abrupt awakening, usually not accompanied by major signs of hunger. When handled comfortably by the simplest of reassurances (covering, cuddling, and changing the baby), it tends to disappear within a few days or weeks. When mishandled, as we will discuss, it can become a severe and annoying problem.

Along with the increase in motor capacity, which the child demonstrates by his ability to sit, to stand, and to walk before the end of his first year, there is a correspondingly increased capacity to utilize food of various kinds and consistencies, as well as to modify the patterns of elimination. The number of voidings and stools diminishes constantly throughout this first year and paves the way (although it does not make the child fully ready) for experiencing the social phenomenon of bowel and bladder training. At least the normalcy of growth permits the child to contain his excreta for longer and longer periods.

A major phenomenon during the first year is the growth of teeth during the latter part of this period. This not only prepares the way for a different kind of food satisfaction, but also leads to a form of behavior which is not always well received by parents. The nursing mother may complain of the infant's biting, and the frightened mother may see the presence of teeth as a prodrome of an attack of either herself or the siblings. It is very apparent, therefore, that the simple sucking activity of the early part of this year develops into biting and a rather aggressive form of activity that leads into the second year. The problems relative to this relate more to the second year, although it is apparent that the phenomenon of biting relative to breast-feeding is a crucial aspect of the child's development. It is one of the important steps in the child's understanding of himself as an individual. The child becomes aware of this separation when the parent withdraws from biting during the breast-feeding situation.

Prior to this time it is felt that the child regards the mother's breast as an extension of himself and one which serves only to satisfy his immediate hunger needs. Subsequently, however, the pulling away suggests that there is a change in the relationship and the child, sensitive to this increase in tension, begins to react by some concern. The fact that this phenomenon takes place even in the absence of breast-feeding is of critical importance. It becomes apparent that many parents are bothered merely by the child's biting activity, even though it is not connected specifically with breast-feeding. The reaction of many mothers to the act of teething suggests a good deal of concern about the fact that something new is going to happen. They may express it either in terms of

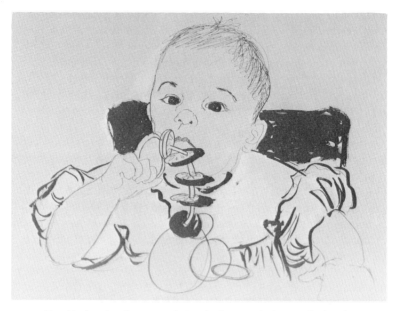

Fig. 4-1. A major phenomena during the first year is the growth of teeth.

being bitten or that the child is in some way attacking the world around him.

This fear of the biting aspect of life transfers over into considerable anxiety about the process of teething itself. There appears to be a very distinct correlation between the way the mother feels about the oncoming act of biting and the amount of anxiety present in the child. The numerous home remedies relative to teething suggest that this is a crucial aspect of the way the mother feels about the care of her infant. On the one hand she is anxious to have the child avoid the pain and discomfort that may come from the protrusion of teeth. Studies of children, however, suggest that in a more objective situation, teething goes on quite comfortably and without any demonstrable concern. It is not clear at the present time how maternal concern and the infant's discomfort do relate, but there is a strong suggestion that this discomfort can be minimized whenever the parent is not concerned as to what is to happen to her and to the world around her as the child begins to demonstrate his aggressive tendencies.

DIFFERENTIATION OF THE WORLD

As noted, in the early sensory equipment of the child, not only is there a lack of organization, but it is quite apparent that there is a lack of perceptual separation of the child from the mother. Studies suggest that the symbiotic relationship of mother to child in early infancy persists in various ways and through various modalities of care. Watch a small child touch the mother whenever threatened by a stranger or cling more closely when a painful experience is anticipated. It is equally apparent, however, that with each increase of sensory capacity the child begins to see the outside world differently and begins to see parts of himself and then, subsequently, parts of other people. Thus, we see during the latter part of the first year the child beginning the painful process of separating himself from the world around him and the difficulties that relate to the concept of independence. It may well be that the impact of this separation leads at times to some of the feeding difficulties and possibly the sleeping difficulty described above. One does see, however, that the infant begins to recognize the world not as a part of himself, but as something which can be approached. Thus, the early taking in of all parts of life changes to a grasping, biting, aggressive capacity which must be lived through in order to perfect the organization of the infant's personality. Clinical experience from children who have had difficulty during this period suggests that the child has the capacity to suffer loss at this time, a loss which may be one of the many prodromata of what is later referred to as sibling rivalry. Other symptoms may also derive from this sense of loss; for example, a feeling of antagonism towards the world whenever things don't go in the desired way.

When this loss is viewed objectively, it is essentially that of the child becoming separated from the mother and having to act in an independent capacity. While this is an extremely healthy act in view of the child's ultimate development, it may be seen by the child as very disastrous. For many children, the loss of the seeming connection with the mother during the latter part of the first year may be emphasized by the arrival of a sibling in the home. In the case of a younger child, the seeming loss of the mother may emphasize the fact that there are other children to whom this particular child must relate and for whom the mother must offer care. Thus, the seeming loss gains a secondary importance in that the child sees it not only as a step toward independence, but as a step towards sharing. As we noted earlier, the infant's general concept of the world around him is characterized by selfishness. The fact that this must change with the passage of time and that the child must share his contact with the mother with others comes as a disturbing feature to many children, particularly where the contact with the mother has not been close and comfortable.

It is perhaps because of these circumstances that the role of the parent in caring for the needs of the small infant has to match the demands of the child. Our normal society considers this to be a giving period; and when this giving is properly accomplished, the child is comfortable and can stand the effects of growing away from the symbiotic clinging to the parent. Thus, the healthy child is prepared for the next step into the second year, where independence and learning become even more critical factors in the process of development.

5

THE FIRST YEAR: THE MOTHER'S
RESPONSE

The presentation of a newborn to his mother elicits a response which is the product of two major groups of feelings. The most immediate concerns the mother's feelings about the pregnancy and delivery through which she has just gone. At its best, the mother views the arrival of the child as a healthy culmination of her efforts during the past nine months. At its worst, the child is regarded the source of a good deal of pain and discomfort, either over that period of time or in the immediate present. The other major group of feelings are those which have been building up throughout the mother's life and have culminated at this point. They concern her anxieties about children, childbearing, family, and especially the sex and wholeness of this particular child.

MOTHER'S INITIAL RESPONSE TO THE INFANT

At no time are the mother's basic feelings about children better demonstrated than in her immediate reaction to the presentation of her newborn. Throughout the pregnancy she has had a variety of expectations of the child, many of them concerned with its sex, others concerned with its health, and other concerned with her capacity to care for the child. When the child is presented to her, one very quickly sees the efforts which she makes to allay her concerns and fears and to prepare herself to handle, care for, and cope with the infant. The very striking demonstration of her expectations is seen in the first questions she asks. Her initial query has to do with the sex of the child, and the response sets a pattern of behavior on her part that will continue throughout the child's life. In varying degrees a mother has some expectations of whether her child will be a boy or a girl; but when she is told definitively, a whole set of reactions come into play that may either assist her in the care of the child or at times interfere with the best use of her own ability.

Her second question usually has to do with the health of the child: "Is it whole?" "Is it healthy?" "Is he breathing well?" The answer to this second group of questions constitutes either a massive release of anxiety from her own sense of responsibility or, if there is some damage, in a great heightening of her tension and a consequent concern about the handling of the child. The child who presents himself at birth with either a congenital handicap or a paranatal distress stirs up great anxiety in the ordinary mother, an anxiety which exhibits itself in the way she handles and feeds and thinks about the child. It is of great importance that the physician be aware of this pair of concerns in order to assist the mother in talking about them and to understand her reactions.

HANDLING THE INFANT

The fact that under ordinary circumstances she is to initiate a period of considerable handling of the child is also subject to certain older determinants that manifest themselves with the immediate presentation of the child. The mother who is comfortable about her own capacity and ability, either by experience or from a sense of general security, takes the child instantly, handles him well, and begins a pattern of social stimulation in care which is necessary for the child's growth. If, however, the mother is confronted by anxieties, either about the baby or about her own ability, the initial handling of the child may be gross, clumsy, and inadequate. There is a growing body of evidence that this initial reaction of the mother sets in the child a pattern of reaction which may lead to some of the irritable and annoying features that can characterize early infancy. Cases are continually being documented of infants responding to the tension in the mother by an irritability and excessive responsiveness which leads to the child's being called hypertonic or resistant. Once this pattern begins, it snowballs with each continuing contact and calls for a tremendous amount of assistance and care to alleviate the tension that the mother presents. Mothers are quite prone to forget their initial response to the child. The physician who can observe it and use it or who can help the mother remember may make it possible to see that it is not only the child's actions that are important.

FEEDING THE INFANT

The mother's capacity is tested next when a decision must be made about feeding. The ordinary mother, anxious to help her child and anxious to care for the child through her own capacity, is usually willing to nurse. Unconsciously, most mothers are aware that the act of nursing is in itself a most pleasurable one both for the child and for herself. While the nutrient value of the nursing experience can be matched by a variety of artificial means, nothing can take the place of the mutual pleasure in suckling and being suckled. As we will note later, certain mothers, particularly those whose personality is characterized by fastidiousness, sense also the pleasurable aspect of nursing but deny it to themselves for the very reason that it is so satisfying. This naturally handicaps the nursing process and leads to dissatisfaction on the part of the child, so the attempt is usually quickly abandoned. It seems important to stress the pleasurable aspect because, usually, this is either denied or repressed. To bring it to the fore and to help the woman become comfortable in it, may become a very valuable part of the whole process. Whatever happens in the early days of the nursing process sets a pattern for subsequent nursing phenomenon and other feeding manners as the child develops.

It is important to realize that the mother who bottle-feeds her infant, for whatever reason, may require as much help, support, an encouragement as the mother who breast-feeds. Whatever the method of feeding selected by the mother, the physician, nurse, or whoever is in the position to help, does a significant service to the mental health of both mother and child by showing interest and respect for such mundane tasks as helping the mother find a comfortable position for herself and the baby, demonstrating to the mother the fact that the infant can actively participate in finding the nipple, utilizing the rooting or orienting reflex, helping the mother who breast-feeds position the nipple and aerola in the infant's mouth for optimal attachment, burping the infant, and, in the case of bottle fed infants, testing the bottle nipple for flow.

POSTPARTUM DEPRESSION

An extremely common reaction pattern in the mother in the immediate postnatal period is a feeling of sadness or depression which varies considerably in degree. It has been postulated that the mother's successful completion of pregnancy leaves her in a vulnerable state and one in which she feels she has accomplished much and wishes to be relieved of the burden of care for a period of time. The fact that she is presented with a newborn infant who demands attention and care is sometimes a matter of considerable concern to her, and she becomes sad at her lack of ability, as well as the fact that other people are not taking care of her. Many mothers have a feeling of loss which aggravates this sense of inadequacy. Quite often this response is alleviated by the care that is given to women in the lying-in situation. At other times, however, and more particularly since early ambulation, the woman is encouraged to get going quickly again, to resume her activities which perhaps include not only the care of the child but the care of the household as well. When this occurs, the temporary relaxation that she would have preferred to enjoy is denied her, and she reacts in a depressed fashion, causing concern for her own safety as well as for the care of the child.

It obviously becomes difficult for the mother who is depressed to offer to the child the kind of care that is so much needed at this particular point. During the early months of the child's life so much of the mother's time is spent in actual physical care of the child that she offers to him, in addition to the nutrient process, a good deal of general stimulation. As time goes on, however, it becomes necessary to add some social and behavioral aspects of stimulation such as is involved in the smile, in the tenderness of holding, and in those activities of general care which are not related either to feeding, changing, or cleaning. That the child needs such stimulation has been demonstrated by a variety of studies and, in general, the mother is happy to offer such stimulation.

THE MOTHER'S AMBIVALENCE

As the child progresses, the mother begins to sense, long before it occurs, the fact that the child, in establishing his own identity, is to a certain extent growing away from her. It is important, therefore, to begin to see early in the child's existence that a phase of this existence includes both a close attachment to the mother and, subsequently, a growing away from her. There are certain mothers who are excellent nurses and handlers of small babies. They enjoy the dependency of the child upon them. They enjoy his social responses. Very early, however, they find that the child is establishing certain responses of his own which will subsequently make him independent. This creates a very strong sense of ambivalence in such a mother because, although she wishes her child to grow up and be independent, it means that he is growing away from her, establishing patterns of his own and no longer dependent on her. This is rarely seen in the early part of the first year but, as the child's ability to sit, stand, and walk increases, one sees a growing apprehension on the part of the mother. The early manifestation of this is seen in the maternal response to the aggressive activity of the child during the latter part of the first year. When he is enabled, by the possession of teeth, to bite, the mother finds herself not only being attacked but being attacked by an independent being. Mothers need considerable understanding about this particular time, especially if they are breast-feeding. A mother's repudiating a child for a developmental pattern over

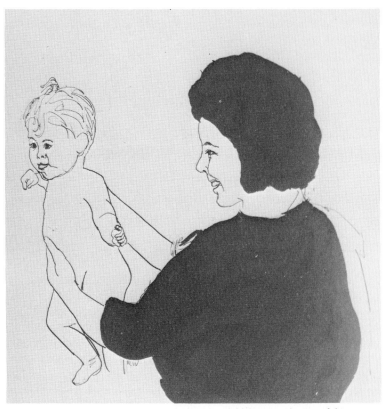

Fig. 5-1. The mother begins to sense that the child has an identity of his own.

which he has very little control sets up two reactions: one, the child's feeling of fear that he has done some harm which he does not comprehend, and, second, a learning that concerns itself with a new capacity to inflict harm. Other experiences in the life of such a child, even during the latter half of the first year, may provoke him to anger against the parent, and he discovers that he has a tool to carry out such aggression.

DISCIPLINING THE INFANT

Even punishment and discipline play a part in the first year of the child's existence. Many parents begin an overly punitive approach to the child quite early. In terms of the infant's capacity to respond, the only power that he has is to become more irritable, cranky, and demanding. The important aspect of this is that the kind of relationship established during the first year is of considerable importance in predicting a subsequent reaction of the child. The parent who feels the need to punish the child for things over which he has very little control merely sets up an irritable pattern of aggressive reaction which will continue throughout the years to come.

SPOILING THE INFANT

Erikson characterizes the first year as one in which a sense of trust or mistrust is built into the personality pattern. The parent has, therefore, the opportunity, not to spoil the child, but to set a pattern of behavior wherein the child can understand that when he has a legitimate request, it is taken care of. Early, the child's omnipotent demands for food or other attention seem to suggest an immediate response. The fact, however, that the child grows and develops a capacity to endure tension within himself makes it possible for the parents to begin to modify their care. They need not jump at the immediate and insistent demands of the child on every occasion. The reaction of some parents to these continuing demands suggest almost a slavery on their part. Such an attitude of slavery is built out of a concern that they are not doing enough for the child or that they have some guilt about their earlier responses to the child. This attitude of fearful guilt (usually not recognized) gives rise to the not uncommon phenomenon of "spoiling." Every culture has different ideas about the extent of spoiling. It is apparent to an outside observer that certain parents cannot tolerate any excess demand on the part of the child, and they try to satisfy it even before it occurs. Such action tends merely to prolong the sense of omnipotence that is normal for the first part of life but which must become modified. Very often the parents cannot modify it themselves, but need the objective pointing out that can come only from an outside source. It is the proper role of the physician to indicate where the demands of the child are normal and usual, and where they have become abnormal and restrictive to the parents. To comply continually with every whim of the child does not in itself produce the sense of trust that is necessary. Rather, the sense of trust grows out of a complete but controlled satisfying of instinctual demands.

The simplest test comes from the observation of such activities and an objective appraisal of whether the parent's response is to alleviate his or her own concern or to do something specifically for the needs of the child. One sees this frequently in parents whose own background or immediate living situation may be considered deprived. The woman who is trying to rear a child without the help of a husband, due either to absence or lack of interest, may pour an excess amount of attention into her care of the child. Such actions are the result of her own loneliness. Such an excess leads to an overinterpretation of the child's demands and an oversatisfaction of them. It does not, in any way, establish a sense of trust, but merely perpetuates the closeness and demandingness of early infancy at a stage in life when such is not necessary. Mothers, particularly in such a situation, find it difficult to see this for themselves, and the physician's objectively pointing this out becomes crucial if the child is to be permitted to grow during the latter half of this first year. The mother has real need of outside observation to avoid falling into the trap which her own loneliness seems to promote.

6

THE SECOND YEAR

The infant's second year is marked by some of the most dramatic changes that he will ever experience. At the beginning of the year he has gotten to his feet and has taken a few steps. His words, if any, are brief and monosyllabic. His capacity to feed himself is rudimentary except for hand-mouth activity. He is basically still dependent. By the end of the year he not only walks but runs; talks and may occasionally use brief sentences; handles the ordinary tools which we use for eating; and in many instances, has some control of his sphincters.

All of this progress in motor and social development is not free of cost and involves more than intrinsic developing. Very profound relationships between himself and the society which surrounds him take place. All of the great gains that occur in his motor progress mark very important stages in the road from total dependence to a partial sort of independence. Such progress does not go without some modification of his desires, instincts, and personal aims by his environment.

MOTOR DEVELOPMENT

In general, society, as represented by the parents, permits a fairly free expansion of his general motor capacity. Parents are pleased to see their children walking, and they, in many instances, encourage such activity by a variety of coaxings and even some interest in a primitive sort of athletic activity. When, however, the child's motor development begins to equip him to explore the adult world, some forces quickly come into play. The mother who was

Fig. 6-1. Encouragement and help is not the same as excessive pressure for high achievement.

happy to see her child toddling across the floor is not quite so happy when his talents lead him past a coffee table or into a cupboard. It is then that her controls begin to come into action and the child learns that advances in motor power have to be judiciously used and that there is for him a rather irrational process of what can and what cannot be done with one's hands, arms, fingers, and feet. Motor power, thus, is often hedged in by a variety of restrictions which make these learning experiences more than mere physical attainment. But motor development is usually well tolerated, and only in the most rare instances are parents sufficiently punitive to keep a child bound to one area. It is true that some children are so restricted that they remain circumscribed (as in a playpen) much longer than others and their curiosity is thus denied them. The area of burgeoning curiosity which has its advent during this second year must be satisfied in order that the child persist and hold to this particular quality. When curiosity is denied at this stage, the deficit may become very notable later on when the desire to explore is manifested as a need for reading and other forms of learning. In essence, this is a time of learning to learn.

SPEECH DEVELOPMENT

In the area of speech, again, the parent tends not to interfere too greatly. Most parents encourage the formation of words. In some parts of our culture very little reliance is placed on speaking, and not much communication occurs. The general tendency, however, is to overstimulate speech rather than to understimulate. The restrictions placed on motor behavior are not seen in the speech area, but, rather, there is encouragement of the child to talk and, in some instances, a tremendous pressure to talk. When the pressure to speak is confused with other areas of punishment, discipline, and control, we sometimes find children expressing their difficulties in confused babbling, too rapid speech, or perhaps an early form of stuttering. It is in this early form of stuttering that one sees the aggressive quality of speech. Such stuttering may be the result of considerable confusion on the part of the child between his desire to get words out and the fear he has of speaking. It is a form of withholding. It is very important to recognize here not only that speech is a very valuable form of communication, but that progress in learning to talk, as in all other progress areas, gets mixed up with other activities, of both control and learning, that are going on at the same time.

FEEDING

Learning to feed oneself properly and learning some control of the sphincters are areas where society very distinctly insists on the modification and specific patterning of maturational and instinctive processes. The specific mores of any culture are imposed through these functions. The modification of feeding activity occurs usually early in the first year. By the time the child is in the latter part of his first year, he is using his hands to bring food to his mouth, and by the end of the first year, most children are able to handle a variety of forms of food, using their hands. In the second year the introduction of various tools that society uses to bring food to the mouth are introduced in keeping with the cultural level of the parents. In a normal course of events, the ordinary child of fifteen months is able to handle a single tool with some dexterity so that spoon feeding (and eventually fork feeding) becomes a simple and easily accepted manner of self-feeding. Feeding and eating, however, are not simple activities in our society. Not only do we place great value in the nutrient quality of foods, but we have tremendous concern about quantities, qualities, and variation in tastes. We are, indeed, a culture very concerned about its mouth and what goes in it and we pay a great deal of attention to phenomena that surround the act of eating. There is, therefore, a wide continuum within our American culture of feeding manners and mannerisms.

It is these cultural aspects of life which impinge upon the child's normal development of the act of self-feeding. The simple use of tools which make life easier is easily accomplished, as noted above. However, there tend to be restrictions which hedge around the use of these tools. One sees this in two forms. First, the emphasis on cleanliness, and second, the proper use of tools when eating. The parental concern about cleanliness reflects itself in such terms as "messy," "nasty," and "dirty." The child soon learns that, from the mother's point of view, messiness is a thing to be avoided. Such restrictions lead the mother who is concerned about dirt to place great emphasis on the manner of eating, to enforce controls, and to punish when the child disobeys. At times, this leads her to take over the feeding process herself, thus denying the child the normal opportunity to learn. It is crucial to mention here that in the expansion of motor ability there is a fairly specific time during which any one motor skill is in ascendency in the learning

Fig. 6-2. Learning to feed oneself properly and learning some control of the sphincters are aspects of second-year development.

process. When the child is thus ready to learn a new skill it is important that he not be denied the opportunity to practice it. A parent who, out of her own fastidious concern about "messiness," takes over the feeding process at this stage denies the child the capacity to learn and may leave him either awkward or rebellious. He may even fight against the skill to be learned.

It is equally true that not being offered the opportunity to use tools leaves the child inexperienced in this area and poses a problem for him later when he is confronted with his peers who are more capable. One sees in such restriction of the child the beginnings of attempts to keep a child immature, babyfied, and dependent. Fortunately, these are areas that are open to correction, so that the opportunity can be given to the child to progress beyond it.

TOILET TRAINING

The other great area where the instinctual life of the child comes in conflict with society revolves around the control of sphincter activity. This is indeed a most confused area. In the normal progress of a child's development one sees the gradual reduction in quantity of the number of voidings and passage of excreta throughout the first, second, and third years. This is an internal rhythm dependent both on the growth of the bladder and of the muscle tone of the bowel, as well as the autonomic control of these two organs by the nervous system. The change is well described as an increasing capacity to delay. It would seem, therefore, most simple to take advantage of the gradually increasing capacity of the infant to withhold material and to institute a measure of training at the time when the child seems ready to understand the addition of some voluntary control to the reflex activity of the sphincters. It is equally apparent that toilet training involves a social relationship with the parent so that the child profits by other motor capacities. The ability to walk and to get to the bathroom by himself, the ability to talk and to hear commands, the ability to change or loosen his clothes, all make for an optimum of training readiness that should be taken advantage of.

It is valuable, however, to think of the process of toilet training as being directed not merely to the expulsion of stool or passage of urine, but also to the retention of these in a social situation which will come. It is not always easy to look ahead to school to realize that the child who is being "toilet trained" is being prepared to retain rather than to expel, since all of the emphasis around the toilet training would appear to come from actual expulsion. It has long been known that the reflex activity of expulsion, particularly of stool, can be established early in the first year of life. However, from the point of view of the child, it seems most important to recognize that the equipment for learning something about voluntary control of the sphincters cannot be carried out until the child is well into the second year. At this time there is available for the learning process all of the abilities that have been mentioned above. By analogy with other motor development, it would seem that voluntary control of the sphincters is established around the turn of the first year. The other adjunctive motor capacities (namely, walking, talking, and the ability to remove one's clothes) become mature during this second year and, therefore, prescribe an optimal time for learning such habit training.

Furthermore, and this we will discuss later in talking about the parent's role, it would seem important that, since this is a learning process, it operates best if freed from other extraneous components that may relate to learning. It certainly is not a time to teach the child something about cleanliness from a highly scientific point of view or even from an emotional point of view. It is equally not a time to introduce punishment.

From the point of view of the child the awareness of defecation increases during the second year. The child begins to realize that something is happening, that something is passing from him. It is a further stage in the differentiation of himself from all the things around him because he becomes aware that a pleasant sensation occurs as he moves his bowels, and then secondarily aware that he is losing something in the process. This aspect of pleasure which the child demonstrates occasionally is very upsetting and a matter of great concern to the parents. Reared in a moral tradition which equates the stool with dirt, the parent becomes bothered by the obvious pleasure that the child takes in passing stool, in withholding it, in playing with it, or in smearing it. A strong moral connotation becomes associated. The parent usually reacts to the child's pleasure by increasing efforts to get the child to eliminate in keeping with the parental wishes. This reaction relates to pleasurable feelings stirred up in the parent which have long since been compensated for by excess cleanliness.

Not only does the child sense a loss in the passage of excreta, but, as he becomes aware that the material is something separate from himself and that it is pleasurable, he thinks of the product of his own elimination as a sort of a gift to the family and particularly to the mother. It may even be considered a part of himself. That most parents do not regard such material as a gift makes for an intrinsic conflict between the child and the people around him—a conflict which sometimes is resolved in the form of punishment or further control. While we do not fully understand how irrational the child must feel the parental actions to be, it is possible to see that this can very quickly become an area where parental discipline conflicts with simple instinctual desires and primitive learning and leads to problems which continue into subsequent years.

Thus the child learns a variety of lessons from this training period. The obvious control of the sphincters is only a part of the whole process. To the child, the lesson of clean and dirty may seem most profound. Unfortunately, these concepts quickly become bound up with the dichotomy of "good" and "bad." All of this can be very confusing to a child, and it is not surprising that he comes out of this period with many mixed feelings. For many children, this year is one in which siblings are born. It is easy to see how the child, trying to establish some independent values, is bothered by the new infant who can merely enjoy dependence. Out of his confused relation to his mother, jealousy is born, which will be discussed later.

7

THE SECOND YEAR: PARENTS' ROLE

The description of the child during the second year suggests that two major processes are occurring. One is the urge toward independence, which means, to some extent, a renunciation of dependence. The other is the learning process, which is accomplished partly by the child himself and partly by his relationships with the world around him. Of these learnings, our society has placed the most emphasis on the modification of the child's patterns of elimination. The confusion of feelings established in the child by this learning is one source of a psychological position called ambivalence. The child experiences ambivalence in terms of his desire to retain or to eliminate. The parent may see it in terms of the child's compliance or stubbornness. Both may fear it as an "ordeal."

At any rate, the major changes in the child's life must be met in some fashion by the parent. Not only is the child, through his search for independence, giving up some of the values of dependence, but the mother must equally give up some of the joys that come to her from the dependent character of the child. No longer does the child totally need her and rely on her for everything. This may, at times, be difficult for her to tolerate. For some mothers, perhaps more than fathers, this sense of loss is great, and they rebel against it by trying to cling to the babyhood of the child. Such simple mechanisms as using baby talk and overdressing the child, postponing learning experiences, and so forth demonstrate the parental desire to cling to the child's babyhood.

Equally, however, one sees parents who urge the child through the learning experiences more rapidly than the child is ready to proceed. The stimulation thus provided is not always well received and one sees the incipient stages of rebellion early in the second year as the child is called upon to master activities that are beyond his developing motor control. This year is well described as a year of *"No."* More important, however, during this year activities which seem to bother the parent and suggest that the child is getting out of hand may lead to later conflictual situations. The child learns the word "no" quickly because it is applied to him in so many situations that seem to him normal, simple, and natural. He is inquisitive and likes to explore the world but is met by *"Stop."* He is curious about himself and explores himself, as well as having an interest in what food he eats and what comes out of him. All these exploratory activities are met with some emphasis on control and modification.

At times, the child's attempts to do things for himself, and particularly to demonstrate his own willfulness in the area of toilet habits, may lead to open warfare between parent and child. Out of such situations the parent demonstrates, and the child becomes aware of, the temporal difference between loving acceptance and angry rejection. Dependent as he has been, he is unaccustomed to the restrictions and demands that are made on him and finds himself in a difficult situation of wanting to be liked by his parents and yet having strong feelings against them. This conflictual situation is a further source of the ambivalent feelings that all of us derive from this particular period. The parents, demonstrating strong aggressive drives in an effort to force compliance, give rise to reactive patterns of belligerence. The powerful drives towards autonomy which the child possesses run into the constricting demands of the parent and may very easily lead to hatred and hostility. The verbs that are used to describe the toilet training process, particularly the word "break," suggest the strength of the parental role in this instance.

The crucial aspect of the struggle which may develop, either around feeding or around the toilet training process, is that it may spread over to other general control activities. The parent, concerned about the direction that the child's groping for independence takes, may feel a very strong need to set rigid and, at times, inflexible limits on his activities. The child's expression of these primitive drives stirs up strong counterforces in the parents and elicits this need to set limits. When such limit-setting coincides with a conflict about the toilet training, the child infers an attitude from the parent that everything is against him and that everyone is angry with him. Out of this feeling of conflict may come a retaliatory aggression or anger on the child's part which will be matched by an increase in parental control. Parents may see the child's aggression as a challenge. For the child, the memories of good experiences conflict with these difficult experiences. There still is a longing, however, for a positive relation, and out of this longing comes a sense of shame or guilt.

The extent, duration, and form of this conflict plays a large part in shaping subsequent personality patterns. Since the conflict sets a new pattern of relations between the child and his parents and in this new pattern there may be a considerable element of anger, hostility has its genesis. Depending upon the manner in which the conflict has occurred, the child expresses this aggression either against other people in the form of fighting back or against himself by turning the aggression inward. With the latter, an overly submissive compliance occurs as a defense. Rather than fight back, the child turns his anger against himself and, to protect himself, becomes overly clean, overly neat, and later on overly orderly in his ways of thinking as well as in his ways of behavior.

There are, however, methods to avoid some of these difficulties. One difficulty to avoid is the pattern of overprotecting the child during the dependent stage. It becomes very obvious that efforts must be made not to prolong this dependence but to permit the child a gradually unfolding independence. Such permission means that the parent must both refrain from overdoing "baby" things and at the same time permit the child to operate alone. Parents who fear their child, for whatever reason, find it especially difficult to let the child discover the world. It takes much urging from the physician to assist these people.

Equally, it is apparent that the child cannot think for himself in many instances, so independence does have to be curbed and controlled and limits have to be set. The crucial thing is not to set these limits harshly and crudely, but to set them progressively so that the child can feel the process of growth and develop the concept that there is an increase in responsibility given to him. It is equally important to take advantage of the child's capacity for motor improvement so that training experiences are neither pushed nor made overly harsh. When the child is permitted to demonstrate a capacity for sphincter training, the act becomes simple and easy. When the operation of such training is not contaminated by the parents' concern about dirt, messiness, and badness, again the act becomes simple and the child learns easily and comfortably.

Some parents, threatened so much by potential problems in the toileting situation, prefer to avoid training their children or if they attempt to train them, are unable to go about it easily and comfortably. In this situation, the child, too, becomes anxious and sometimes is able to detect elements of conflict in the parents. Children are very successful in picking up parental feelings, particularly of anxiety, shame, and guilt. If the general relationship between parents and child is not good enough, the child may use his own behavior as a way of eliciting these feelings in the parent and when successful will be able to manipulate the parent in a very omnipotent fashion. Such power in the hands of the two- to three-year-old is threatening to all concerned. The physician who can discern such a pattern of interaction between parent and child does well to help the parent see what is happening so as not to be susceptible to such manipulation.

By taking advantage of observable motor development, therefore, many of the conflictual situations can be avoided. It is particularly important to avoid conflict over the toilet training experience because many other potential conflict areas can quickly be established in this aspect of life. If the child can come through this period of life with some self-satisfaction in both his growth and learning, he will be in a good position to enter the next learning period which involves a wider use of his social and motor activity. If, however, the impact of the training experience is negative, there will be aroused in the child a deep sense of shame which he will carry with him as he approaches other stages of his social growth. This becomes particularly important as the child becomes more sexually aware of himself and gets into the area of self-exploration and the need to understand more of his anatomical existence.

A three-and-a-half-year-old boy was seen because of stubbornness, refusal to go to the potty, temper tantrums, and an enlarged abdomen that was found to be filled with feces. He was very neat and was preoccupied with trains. Both parents were striving, well organized individuals who worked. From the time he was eight months old to one-and-a-half years of age, the child had been cared for by a baby-sitter, during which time toilet training was attempted but unsuccessful; he refused to sit on the toilet. The baby-sitter was a large, aggressive woman. Because of temper tantrums and stubbornness, the child was often spanked by both mother and father. In his general development this boy was advanced in almost all ways, spoke clearly, and was skillful in the use of his hands. The mother was pregnant at the time he was first seen and related that she had similar difficulties with her bowels as a child and was often spanked.

The child was an intelligent, good-looking boy who left his parents easily coming into the playroom. He drew pictures and painted, threw darts, and told the examiner that he would like to have a baby and that when he grew up he would like to be a sister. He was frightened of the toilet, saying, "down boo-ba." He expressed a liking for his own bowel movement but did not go to the potty. He was, however, able to flush a piece of paper down a toilet and seemed intently interested as he watched it go down.

It was felt that he and his parents had reached a stalemate and were locked in conflict about his bowel functioning. His parents wanted to take it away and he wished to keep it to himself. The clinical material suggested that he was frightened of losing the bowel movement and also that he himself might be swallowed up in the toilet. This would explain his refusal to sit on the toilet and his need to control all aspects of bowel functioning.

Several recommendations were made to the parents as follows:

1. Show some admiration of your son's bowel movements even if they are passed in his pants; help him take over control of the toilet rather than being forced to use it.

2. Discontinue spanking; offer approval and reinforcement of positive achievement at every opportunity.

3. Give constant reassurance regarding the new baby and the continued possibility of the son's remaining in favor with his parents.

4. Foster a better relationship with the father.

5. Discontinue all anally and bowel-oriented types of therapy—no enemas or cathartics, no inspections.

6. Return for follow-up evaluation one month after new baby is born.

The mother wrote three weeks later as follows:

"Our progress with Marvin—he talks more freely about his bowel movements. He has had several (about three or four) large movements. He says they are for me, so I praise him very highly. If I ask why he hasn't given me a movement for a while, he says, 'I'm not filled up yet.'

"The other night my husband asked him why he did all his big ones for me and none for him to see, and Marvin said, 'Guess you'll just have to stay home from work to see one.' He still draws his feet up and strains, occasionally goes to another room to do this, but it does seem to be much better.

"The first bowel movement after our last visit with you was the largest I have ever seen (adult or child), it was about eleven or twelve inches long and about two and one-half inches in diameter. It didn't seem to bother him to pass it, he just called to me and said, "I did a big poop for you.""

8

THE PRESCHOOL YEARS

When the child has accomplished the major growth and learning of the second year, he is ready for a period of the exploration of the world. During the next few years, prior to the onset of formal learning at about the age of five or six, the child is in a period of steady, even physical growth and a considerable expansion of the quality of his motor apparatus. The refinement of motor performance that takes place in these years makes it possible to explore the world around him and to be comfortable in the act of doing so. It is not a matter of learning new skills, but a matter of refining skills in walking, running, riding, talking, and in using his hands.

The steady growth and expansion of the motor system is matched by a curiosity which extends into all phases of the social sphere. At the end of the second year the child is often playing with one or more peers, but as time goes on his social contacts normally expand and the groups in which he can feel comfortable grow larger. Thus, in a nursery school or neighborhood situation one sees a gradual enlarging of the numbers of the child's contacts. Such social exploration is aided by his communication. The child who has not been stunted by an overprotective dependency is capable of conversing and communicating with his peers. Such communication

Fig. 8-1. At the end of the second year the child is often playing with one or more peers.

grows rapidly during these years, and the greater the number of satisfying peer contacts the child has, the more comfortably he grows.

SEXUAL CURIOSITY

During this period most children have a rather marked curiosity, a curiosity that turns to people much as it did to things when he was a fifteen-month-old baby. The curiosity starts primarily with himself. He learns more and more about the manner in which he can use his body and the way in which his body appears. The boy becomes interested, curious, and eventually fascinated by his urinary apparatus, particularly his penis. The girl, less comfortable in this area, becomes aware, as does her brother, of the differences between the sexes. The impact of such discoveries is extremely important. The child is not only curious but highly impressionable, and the discoveries that he makes about himself must be corroborated by seeing other children and by trying to understand the relationship between himself and adults. The vulnerability which the child feels is enhanced at this point because it is apparent that not only is he small and subject to adult discipline and control, but that this apparatus of his is relatively small and unimportant.

The child's initial discovery of his genitals is probably associated with a vague pleasant feeling which he learns can be enhanced by friction, rubbing, or other activity. This quickly leads to a primitive masturbatory activity. However, it is equally apparent that as soon as a child makes such a discovery, the outside world frequently moves in to manifest critical attitudes about manipulation of the genital area. The amount of anxiety stirred up in the parent will relate to the parent's own concern about genital activity; but in general these concerns are communicated rapidly, quickly, and often powerfully. So it is that the child's interest in his genitals and the genitals of others acquires a significance far beyond his initial pleasure because of the level of social tone which is demonstrated by parents, peers, and others.

On the whole, the boy's satisfaction with the discovery of his genitals and that of his fellows makes life fairly comfortable. The girl, lacking even breasts, which she can see on the adult female, has very few compensations to assist her at this particular period ot time. A boy, however, not infrequently demonstrates a considerable concern once he learns the anatomy of the female genitalia. The absence of something of which he is a proud possessor leads him to a state of fear and concern, lest what happened to the girl happen to him. It is not easy for the mind of the small child to understand the basic anatomical differences, and the fact that the girl may have been like him but lost something is a constant and recurrent theme in the fantasies of these small children.

FANTASY

One of the characteristic mental activities of this particular age period is fantasy. Such fantasies probably grow out of the numerous discrepancies that the child sees between himself and the world around him. When he is small, he is comforted by big people; but as he gains in his motor control and becomes a part of the bigger world, the differences between his body and that of adults become increasingly dramatic in the fact that adults can do more things, are more powerful, are bigger, and are more controlling. Whatever he does, adults "boss him around." So the child begins a pattern of fantasy that continues for many years. Much of this activity is designed to help the child master his concerns. The fantasies, however, of this particular period are notable for the fears they contain. Not only in nightmares, but also in the daydreams of children of this period there are a variety of fear situations connected with genital attack as well as fears of destruction at the hands of older, larger, and bigger people.

The child meets some of these fears with a very rich and active playing-out of the activities of older people and playing-out particularly those areas which concern him. Thus we see little girls dressed up like their mothers and little boys play-acting many of the roles of adult male. Thus, also, we see the highly fascinating game of playing doctor wherein legitimately one can explore, become curious, and, at times, attack members of the same and other sex in a fashion which suggests a profound interest in the whole of the genital behavior of life.

CONSCIENCE FORMATION

But also during this period we begin to see the child taking on impressions of the behavior of adults and building them into his own personality. The rudiments of a conscience expressed in behavior are seen early. Even in the first year, children learn not to do things when they are repetitively punished or shamed. However, in this particular period we see the impact of parental discipline being built into the control the child has over his own activity. In this manner he picks up the moral percepts of his family and peers and begins to act in accordance with them. The extent and impact of the parental teaching modifies the conscience of the child. Thus, the formation of the conscience depends not only upon the way the child receives and perceives the demands of the parents, but also on his general relationship with the parents. For example, if the child has been in a conflictual situation with the parent during the second year, the moral percepts offered during the third and fourth years are often either ignored or rebelled against. The parent may again see this as a stubborn opposition. The elaboration of the conscience depends upon the manner in which the child has completed an earlier experience of life and, thus, the principle of one stage building on another becomes notable. In some instances, the voice of conscience may resemble the voice of fear, especially if the child's feeling about adult behavior is related only to punishment, control, and limit-setting. More hopefully and more normally, the voice is that of love, wherein the child has an adequate respect for the parent.

THE CONFLICT CALLED OEDIPAL

Toward the end of this period the child's awareness of the discrepancy between himself and adults takes on a new form. The child attempts in a primitive way to assume an adult role and comes into conflict with other members of the family, particularly the father and the mother. One sees this in the boy who tries to assume that he is as good as the father and that he can take the father's place with the mother. Such an assumption includes also the child's difficulty in giving up a dependence on the mother and in relinquishing the comfort of female protection in order to become a male. The boy child, therefore, is torn between his love for (and dependence upon) the mother and some fear of the father. At the same time, he is trying to be a rival to the father. It becomes obvious to the boy that rivalry is in itself a frightening experience and that for him to attempt to be like the father may lead to a retaliation on the part of the father. The struggle existing in the child's mind during this time constitutes what is described as the Oedipus situation.

The normal resolution of this difficulty comes when the boy makes a more comfortable identification with the father, an identification which allows him to take on some of the attributes of manliness and pride himself in an association with the father. Just as the child resolves fear fantasies by acting out these fantasies with his peers, so through work and shared work activity the boy learns to be like the father, to enjoy working with him, and to carry out the normal masculine role activities, be they sports, play, or work.

For the girl, this period, too, is marked by a rivalrous situation when she attempts to be to the father what the mother normally is. The intrusion of the girl into a jealous situation with her mother may give satisfaction if her advances are approved by the father. But it may also give rise to a certain amount of fear lest the loving dependency which she has for the mother be lost in the process. The girl, too, must resolve her internal struggle by forming a new identification and a new establishment of a female role patterned after the comfortable role of her mother. Here again, playing out a fantasy situation plus a shared activity becomes of considerable importance. The deviations in this process will be discussed in Part III.

At these periods the opportunity for the parent to share his or her ordinary activities with the child becomes of prime significance. It not only builds a complete picture in the child's mind of what it is to be an adult and how pleasurable it can be, but it establishes a useful and nonthreatening control by the adult in the child's mind. What was referred to earlier as conscience formation becomes a crucial part of this progress; and as the child takes on the behavioral characteristics of the parent by identifying with him, he takes on also the usefulness of the parent's attitudes as a controlling device during the time when the parent is no longer with him. Such control enables a child to handle himself in situations outside of the family and makes it possible for him to have a set of guides which are intrinsic to himself but which he has learned and implanted in his mind from parental observation and parental demonstration. His own fantasies have also played a part in building this control. Under such circumstances he is prepared for the next step, that of the vastly important job of academic learning.

It becomes apparent from our own conduct that our value systems and controls have an automatic quality. So ingrained are they that they operate without thought or voluntary control. They have become incorporated into a portion of our mental activity that is not under conscious domain. The simple symptom of the blush demonstrates, however, both the relation to forbidden thoughts and the constantly active power of these unconscious thought processes. It is these deep-lying mental activities that make us anxious and guilty—especially when our buried desires conflict with our overt and consciously expressed thoughts or plans. The persistence of fears, angers, and desires in the unconscious serves to modify conscious learning as well as conscious action. The store of these unconscious feelings grows with each passing stage.

PLAY

When children are having fun, and especially when they are doing things that happen spontaneously out of their own initiative and with no particular goal in sight and with no particular structure or rules, we generally acknowledge that they are playing. With the advent of school the distinction between play and work is abruptly drawn, sometimes much too abruptly, so that there is no smooth transition between play and work. If the distinction between play and work is drawn too abruptly or made too dogmatically, play and work are contrasted in terms of pleasure and pain, or good and bad, or right or wrong. Then there is stagnation in both areas, and the child is unable to play or to work, with extreme forms of aggressive, uncontrolled, impulse expression alternating with ritualized drab, unsatisfying work. Play offers a chance for the individual to relate the diverse parts of himself, including some of his impulses and conflicts, to the individuals and circumstances around him. Beyond the period of infancy, play is an activity that takes place within a peer group culture, whether it be of children or adults. When adults "play with children" their role is quite different than it would be if they were playing with their own peers. They actually are helping children to play and are giving them permission to do so. When children, on the other hand, prefer "playing" with adults, very often we discover that they are avoiding true play with their peer group. It is interesting that children's play often is an attempt on the part of adults to reenter childhood.

Play which is characteristic for each age presents us clues to the level of functioning of the child and the relationship of the child to others in his environment. For example, the earliest kind of play is observed in the first few days, following feeding. Infants usually do not fall asleep immediately following feeding, but are often more alert than at any other time, at least for two or three minutes. During this period, mothers talk to their babies, look at them, move, and the infant very often is able to follow movements of the mother's face. Sometimes a smile is observed. This early play period provides an opportunity for the infant to respond to the sequences of sensory stimulation by the mother. Later on, smiling games are invented by the parent. These serve as a means by which the infant anchors himself to social contact. The characteristic game of peek-a-boo provides an opportunity for the mastery of separation of self from someone else and establishing reunion following separation, thus dealing with one of the basic anxieties in all humans, the fear of loss of human relatedness.

Many of the early play activities and games engaged in the first year or so of life are bodily games. They help the infant gain a sense of his own body limits and functions in relationship to the outside world. This period of life is spoken of by Erikson as "autocosmic" play. In the second and third year of life, the infant learns to manipulate small objects with his hand. He uses speech and fantasy in his play activities. This is "microcosmic" play. Later, when play comes to have a social meaning, with relatedness to other children one can observe "macrocosmic" play. There are characteristic play activities for each of the older age periods. All of these provide an opportunity for reexperiencing anxieties of the past, mastering them, and preparing for events of the future.

Observing a child's play provides the observer an opportunity to witness in the daytime what the child does at night in his dreams. Play, thereby, becomes the vehicle by which the child makes himself known to the observer. The elements of conflict, as well as mastery and synthesis, are illustrated in his play. The sources of his anxiety, his deepest primitive wishes, together with his current and future expectations, are illustrated.

TRANSITIONAL OBJECTS AND PHENOMENA

One of the most common and easily observed manifestation of the child's transitional object relations is to be found in his activities with the favorite soft toy, blanket, piece of wool, or such, described by Dr. Donald Winnecott. The child takes these objects to bed with him, places them near his face, often they are rubbed up against the child's face and at these times the child seems relatively oblivious to other things going on around him. This phenomenon is illustrated by Linus' attachment to his blanket in the comic strip "Peanuts" by Charles Schultz. The universal popularity of the comic strip originates in the awakening of the meaningfulness of Linus' experience in each of us. The earliest origins of this behavior are found in the infant's nursing experiences, not in the actual taking in of nutriment or the sucking of the bottle or breast which contains the milk, but in the accessory events which surround feeding, such as thumb-sucking, pressure and tactile sensations on the face and snout area, kneading the blankets with the hands, and holding onto something during the nursing experience. These accessory activities come to occupy an intermediary position between the infant and his mother. Engaging in them provides the illusion of a basically secure anchorage to the mother. The infant's first learning occurs in the feeding situation when some of these accessory activities become available to him prior to the actual taking in of nourishment. These are the first remembered cues to socially gratifying experience. Later, as the child faces the fear of losing the mother, intense attachment to objects which are provided at moments of great anxiety takes place. The child very often gives these objects a name.

9

THE PRESCHOOL YEARS:
PARENTS' ROLE

DISCIPLINING THE CHILD

The emotional development of the preschool child poses more subtle situations for the parent than do the dramatic activities of the second year. Many of the problems of discipline confronting the parent during the second year continue throughout this preschool period. Handling these disciplinary problems depends greatly on the manner in which discipline was enforced during the early stage of learning and striving for independence. The parent who was either harsh, vindictive, overly punitive, or demanding during the early period, will probably carry out the same standards of behavior during the preschool years. However, as the reactions of the child become more organized, greater counteraction is posed, and the parent is likely to become more and more dismayed as the child exerts his rebelliousness, antagonism, and other displays of temper. From the loosely organized temper tantrums of the second year, the child may well proceed to gross forms of disobedience and stubbornness.

REACTIONS TO CHILD'S SEXUAL CURIOSITY

Equally perplexing to the parent may well be the child's curiosity about himself and his body. The naturalness of this curiosity is rarely apparent to the parent whose own sexual standards prohibit such behavior. It cannot easily be accepted as the simple learning experience which it must be to the child. The pleasure, even when obvious, is not well tolerated. It is not surprising, therefore, that the appearance of this exploration leads to a parental response which varies from tolerance to a rather extreme form of suppression. Whatever the reaction of the parent, the attitude involved is quickly communicated to the child. From the point of view of the physician, the manner in which this attitude is presented to the child is much more important than the words that are used or the parent's supposed way of talking to the child.

Subtle communications between parents and children are omnipresent during all stages of the learning process. They become particularly important as a child moves into a learning experience that includes moral values which may be in contradistinction to his own natural investigations. At this period in life, the child is highly impressionable and is much more concerned about the reaction of his parents than he was earlier. The early reactions of the child were more diffuse and less organized. At this point in time they may become highly accurate in direction. As the child receives these impressions, he begins to build them into a pattern of his own behavior and stores them in his own unconscious reservoir of memories.

It is not easy, therefore, for the parent to approach this period in life with equanimity. The job of a physician, at this period, is not relegated to increasing or decreasing the speed of stimulations of the child, but rather to helping parents to understand their own feelings relative to the emotional phases of growth that have been described. It is one thing to encourage the mother to permit her child to go through the learning experience of feeding. It is another thing to assist parents to permit a child to go through the emotional experience of self-exploration and self-stimulation. Yet, this is the parent's responsibility at this particular stage of growth; and only when the parent is comfortable with the fact that the child must know something about himself can he permit the child to go through this learning experience without interference.

This period is a time when the child, perforce, must have certain learning experiences which can take place only in a peer culture. It is not possible for the parent to push this learning along, nor is it reasonable for the parent to try to hold it back. The former approach has often, unfortunately, contaminated some of the learning experiences. Parents, feeling that children ought to be learning something about the sexual nature of life, expose themselves to the child in a manner which can only be stimulating. That the child must learn something about his own nature and self is patent; however, the child must learn this within the range of his own experience and at his own level. To be exposed to parental stimulation through the presence of nudity or overt demonstrations of sex can only confuse the child, who himself is impressed by his smallness and, at times, his meanness. Therefore, the overuse of sexual stimulation can be as harmful as the suppression of sexual interests by the more prudish and concerned parent.

The latter usually demonstrates concern by a series of prohibitions. These prohibitions range all the way from moral concerns to an overt attack on the child. The boy who innocently plays with his penis is threatened with dire punishment (up to that of cutting it off) if he does not cease. Such prohibitions become, in themselves, highly vindictive, stir up intense fear in the child, and lead to a major anxiety which in itself is unwarranted by the child's actions and feelings.

It is not surprising, therefore, that within our culture generally, the moral tone of disapproval of all kinds of sexual explorations leaves its mark on children. They very quickly learn that to demonstrate openly the exploration of self or others leads to punishment, stigma, and shame. The child soon learns that these pleasurable activities must be carried out under cover. Thus, begins an intense act of suppression, a suppression which leads eventually to a complete loss of conscious memory for the experience.

We have already noted that these memories are stored in the

unconscious. Studies of older individuals have perforce led us to the feeling that such suppression is a powerful mechanism of society and that it causes in children an anxiety which becomes buried, but is nonetheless in existence. It is the dynamic action of this loss of memory that both leads to an underlying anxiety and becomes the powerful force that remains within our unconscious area of thinking. It is not surprising that fantasy grows out of this suppression and that the fantasy begins to compensate for the suppression that the parents force upon the child.

The median route of tolerance of the natural instincts of a child becomes once more the manner of comfortable parental approach. This does not mean completely giving in, but, rather, helping the child to understand the usual limits which society prescribes. This obviously depends on the manner in which parents talk with their child. It also relates to his age and stage of comprehension. Unfortunately, many parents, by early punitive actions, destroy their opportunities to relate to their children later.

FOSTERING THE CHILD'S SEXUAL IDENTIFICATION

The parental approach to the latter part of this developmental period is less well understood. It is apparent that each child must, for himself, work through an understanding of his relationship vis-à-vis his two parents. In considering the problems of the boy who must, perforce, give up his mother and adopt the mannerisms and personality of a male, it is important to recognize the different roles of the two parents. From the point of view of the mother, the job of giving up the boy is a serious one. For many mothers this is a normal, comfortable, and easy process; they are anxious that the father become a friend of the boy and act as his mentor through the remaining years of his life. They are, however, somewhat loath to part completely with their sons, and it is not necessary that they do so.

It is important, however, that the mother not carry on the close and clinging relationship characteristic of the early years. In the pathology to be described later we see that certain mothers tend to continue to infantilize their sons and then build them into substitutes for the father. This takes place for a variety of reasons; and when it does, it is not only stimulating to the boy but binds him to the mother in a form which does not permit the normal development of his masculine role.

In the normal course of events the mother relinquishes her control over the boy and permits him greater and greater association with the father so that he can conquer his concern and fear about the father and gradually identify with him. Obviously, this needs a commensurate activity on the part of the father. Many men have long waited for their boy to come to them and "be a man." When this occurs in a gradual process, the boy makes a comfortable identification. At any rate it is necessary that there be available to the boy some contact with the father, either through sporting activity, intellectual activity, or just companionship, that makes it possible for him to be a male with a male and gradually shape a new pattern. The mother aids this process greatly by setting a standard of what she expects a man to be. This includes, not the sexual aspects of masculinity, but, rather, the more ordinary aspects of maleness as seen in work or sport. Even in the absence of a father, the boy can learn what his mother expects a man to be like in every area except adult sex relations.

The mother's role with the girl is often easier, because she can gradually assist her to develop her own femininity through the activities that are customary for the female. The father may, however, be quite bothered by some of the amorous approaches of his daughter, and it is important that her advances be met with friendliness and calmness and that he neither overstimulate nor totally reject her. Again, there is a wise middle road of approach that is consistent throughout the entire growing stage of the child. Pathologically, one sees fathers who overly accept this new approach of the daughter and foster it in a stimulating fashion. Equally, we see fathers who are bothered or embarrassed by the fact that their daughter suddenly becomes more clinging and tend to force her from them in a rejecting fashion. Of the two, the latter perhaps does the least harm but, at the same time, there

Fig. 9-1. The mother can gradually assist the girl in achieving femininity.

is a comfortable, tolerant approach that makes a stage of friendship without either love or rejection.

Two of the prototypes of mishandling are exemplified in the tomboy and the sissy. The tomboy immediately suggests a very strong impact of the father on the daughter which denies the mother the opportunity to rear her girl in her own image. The boy sissy implies some rejection of the father or some overenforcement of maternal attachment which demands that the boy cling to her and become more womanly than masculine. It is patent that both of these extremes are to be avoided; and when one begins to see them, it should be cause for investigation of the kind of role the parents are playing in the life of the child.

10

THE SCHOOL YEARS

A child entering school faces certain new situations. During this period of his life there continues the resolution of the identification problem which is noted in the preschool child. Much of the establishment of a pattern of maleness or femaleness takes place during this period of time when the child is newly exposed to a peer culture. In the process of establishing his own identity, the child rapidly begins to build up and to incorporate a sense of the moral and ethical values of his society. He assimilates, so that they become an integral aspect of his personality, feelings of rightness, wrongness, goodness, badness, and even health and unhealth.

All of these processes of natural growth in the child are necessary to equip him to deal with the larger society that he faces in the school. Commensurately, the school offers the child a new kind of culture, one of competition with his peers which is completely different from, although it builds on, the peer culture of the home and his relationship with his parents.

PROBLEMS OF SEPARATION FROM MOTHER

In going to school the child faces three general groups of problems. The first comes with entry into the school situation. For many children this takes place in a nursery school setting, but the more formal aspect of the academic elementary school may re-demand the need to separate himself from the parents, again particularly the mother. The act of separation is not a simple one. The child is going through a stage of breaking off the dependent relationship with the mother, a fact that applies to both boys and girls. Suddenly the shift in dependency is dramatically enhanced by his entry into a culture where his peers are important and where a new standard of behavior must exist. He feels that he can no longer rely on the protective aspect of the maternal role. This is much more true in the elementary school than it was at the nursery school level. The separation is complicated because the parent also has some concern about giving the child up, which will be dis-cussed in the subsequent chapter.

From a medical viewpoint, there appears a group of symptoms relative to the anxiety of making the total separation and going out on his own. Some children become extremely anxious and manifest it by either overt acts of temper or, more commonly, acts which connote fear. Nightmares predominate at this particular period of time, and the child may develop a daytime concern about going to school or staying in the school. Unchecked, this becomes the more demonstrable symptom of school phobia. For some children separation poses considerable anxiety and fear about being in a school. It is quite obvious that such fear interferes with the learning process and may dominate the child's mind during the time that it continues. The more the child is dependent on the parent, the more this anxiety presents itself. It may be manifest by a rather severe form of concern which leads to an avoidance of school or a carry-over of anxiety into the home. The anxiety in the home is manifest either by nightmares, by an intensification of sibling rivalry, or by an overt antagonism against the parents. From the preventive point of view this relates to the intensity of the de-pendency state; from the therapeutic point of view it relates to the capacity of the mother to permit the child to free himself and yet remain in a normal situation.

Fig. 10-1. The entry of a child into school poses certain situations that did not exist prior to this time.

PROBLEMS OF ADAPTATION TO SCHOOL CULTURE

The second phase of the child's experience in school has to do with adapting himself to the culture of the school. This culture is made up of a variety of components. There is the new authority who substitutes for the parent and whom the child sees in the image of the manner in which he has been handled by the parent. There is the classroom and the demands that the classroom puts on the child. These may have to do with time, organization, completion of task, and, in general, a relationship to others. Finally, there is the relationship to others as manifested by the larger social group of the peers. For many children this aspect of living is a highly acceptable one. A child transfers a good image of the parent to the teacher and accepts the new authority. The child welcomes the organization of life as demonstrated by a schedule, by the organization of classes, and by a form of learning which, in itself, is stimulating. The child welcomes the new group of peers (and is welcomed by them) not only because they are socially stimulating, but because they fit in with his need to get away from the close pressures of his newly established relationship with his parents.

This latter point is a crucial one and often overlooked as to its value to the child. Inasmuch as the child is going through the difficult experience of establishing himself as a male (or herself as a female) in the close-knit family group, the fact that other children are sharing this experience and can, in their own fashion, talk about it is stimulating and healthy. The child feels comfort in the fact that other individuals of his same size, shape, and age are exposed to the same problems and difficulties that he is; therefore, he draws strength and value from the experience. It is not surprising, therefore, that children begin quickly to build up the dichotomy between home and school as two separate, but equally important, cultures. Talk to the child of this age and you will see that he is full of his experiences about schooling, and perhaps equally full, but more reticent, about his experiences at home. They are maintained in two separate channels, and the child does not necessarily talk about one in the other situation unless forced or pressed by either parent or teacher.

It is apparent, therefore, that the child is dividing his experiences; yet, each becomes of value and each has its part to do in shaping his personality. For some children, whose home experiences have been uncomfortable, school with its new peer culture and social group provides a welcome relief from some of the difficulties in home existence. For other children, the various difficulties they meet in the classroom may well be compensated for by the comforts of home. The danger, which we have mentioned earlier, of home being a place where comfort is mainly overprotection is not this sort of compensation. In such homes oversolicitude negates the value of outside contacts.

PROBLEMS OF ACADEMIC LEARNING

The third general area of experience offered by the school is that of academic learning. Here, both intellect and emotion become important. It is grossly apparent that the basic capacity of the child to learn depends upon his constitutional endowment. The pressures of learning force a very quick and clear realization of the extent of these abilities. For the child who fails in this particular experience, a sense of overwhelming anxiety and discomfort arises that is unmatched by previous experience. Many children who have gone comfortably through the preschool years find themselves confronted with the academic problem of learning and not being equal to it. When this occurs, a sense of failure develops which may pursue the child for a long period to come. Contrariwise, the child whose intellectual equipment is sufficient for the task, who is supported by his peer culture, and who adapts to the living situation of the class, finds himself in the very happy atmosphere of developing a capacity to work and a sense of what Erikson calls "industry."

But there is another aspect of learning which depends, not on constitutional endowment, but on the psychological set which the child brings to the learning years. We have noted that the second year sets patterns for learning. If the child has had difficulty with that particular early learning experience, he may develop a concern which carries into later learning. The preschool years contribute their anxieties relative to feelings about size and sex. When he approaches the symbolic processes of spelling and reading he may be bothered by the older worries. At times, some of them totally interfere with the learning process and especially may make the crucial learning of reading an impossibility. A variety of things particularly interfere with reading. They will be discussed later on but, suffice to say, the child who cannot face new experiences, the child who has difficulty with symbolization, and the child who is made anxious by whatever he learns may have difficulty in the very important act of using letters, numbers, and words. We have seen how parents can suppress sexual curiosity, but it is equally true that the suppression of curiosity in general may lead to a child who is unwilling to look at or delve into any of the valuable aspects of knowledge that demand a natural, active, and curious mind.

A certain group of children carry over the stimulation of the Oedipal situation into the activities of the school situation. This is particularly true of boys when parental sexual stimulation is carried beyond the bounds of ordinary propriety. For instance, a mother who, having either rejected or lost her husband, may cling to her son in a manner more appropriate for another adult and set up a stimulation in the boy that becomes intolerable. This stimulation carries over into restless, anxious, neurotic behavior in the classroom which interferes not only with the child's own learning, but the learning of the peer group. Such children become a serious problem for the teacher. The child's anxiety is met by the teacher's repressive attempts with the result that he becomes the *bête-noire* of the classroom and suffers accordingly.

Other children who have difficulty in the learning process are those whose resolution of the ambivalent paradox of the second year was accomplished by turning their hostility inward. We have already described these children as compulsive, overly self-demanding, and often self-punishing. Such punishment may be manifested in an intense desire to please the parent, particularly with high marks and other evidences of great progress. When, however, they are immersed in the actual process of learning itself, they may find that their need to be perfect interferes with their learning. Unfortunately, as their desire to be perfect rises, their anxiety rises commensurately, which interferes with their production. Although they are capable of great learning experiences, they cannot express it, and they fail on examinations. This is a very unfortunate group of children, not only because of the personal experiences but because the problem is so deep-rooted. Some relief from parental pressures often modifies the situation, but frequently it is not enough to assuage the internal concern of the child.

Finally, there is a group of children who, because of a punitive up-bringing, carry the chip of aggression forever on their shoulders. This, too, interferes with learning, not only for themselves but for the other children whom they annoy. This will be discussed later.

As noted earlier, the peer contacts of this age make it, for many children, a very positive period. Play changes to sports and athletics. Fantasy changes to realistic performance. Many children recall it as a very happy time, and for many the base in learning is substantial and highly worthwhile.

At the age of eight, John was transferred to a new school and entered third grade. He encountered a more cohesive group of classmates but also a group more accepting of individuals than that to which he had been accustomed. The new group demanded both good school performance and participation in sports. Excellent in the former, he had always shunned the latter. To his surprise, he was not permitted to remain aloof. He was constantly challenged by the group with the support of the teacher. Feeling this support, he made efforts he thought impossible. The change in his participation did not occur overnight. By the end of a year, however, he was willing to expand efforts in play that startled his parents. His own pleasure was the tangible reward of the new interaction between him and his fellows.

11

THE SCHOOL YEARS: PARENTS' ROLE

PARENTAL SEPARATION ANXIETY

In primitive societies the period that we describe as the beginning of the school age consists of a variety of preparatory rites designed to make the child a part of society. In our own more specialized society we have delegated these preparations to many technicians, chief among them the teachers. It is quite possible that even in these primitive tribes parents have felt various resentments as their children, particularly their sons, became initiated into the tribal activities. Certainly today we find that with the onset of any schooling process there is a certain amount of apprehension on the part of the parents, again particularly the mother, about releasing the child and permitting him or her to go into new social spheres. Some of this apprehension concerns the ability of the child to cope with the group and to master the processes of learning. A greater part of the apprehension consists in giving up her personal role of handling, caring for, and even relating to the child. The mother is naturally concerned that the teacher cannot understand her child as well as she has and certainly cannot offer him the same warm relationship that she has given.

It is not surprising, therefore, that separation anxiety, referred to in our discussion of the child, has a very large component of maternal and sometimes paternal concerns. Again we see a continuum from those parents who stubbornly refuse to give up their child to those who happily kick the child out and assume no further responsibility for him. It is quite normal to have some apprehension and to make some effort to hang on to the child when he spends much of his day away from the home. In a usual solution of this situation the home continues to set certain standards and offer certain rewards, while the school provides other kinds of experiences and a new sort of relation. The physician must be alert for the mother who does cling and who feels unwilling to give up the protective role she has established.

Parental Ambivalence to Teacher. One representation of the parent's ambivalence is seen in our current cultural phenomenon, the PTA. One might well suspect that teachers would never have invented the PTA since they feel no need for the shared kind of experience that the parent demands. Indeed, in some instances the motives of parents in this function are questionable. On the one hand, there is the virtuous motive of a shared experience between parents and the instructor. On the other, there is the feeling that the teacher is going to do something to the child that the parent does not want. The organization, therefore, serves as an arena in which the two protagonists can settle their difficulties. More insidious is the suspicion that the parent feels the need to spy on the teacher in order to make sure that the parent's warrants are being carried out.

One aspect of the child's participation very quickly points up the struggle. In order to participate well in school, the child must establish a sense of loyalty to the school and the teacher. A strong relationship is sometimes established. The mother can then become understandably concerned if every suggestion that she makes is countered with a quotation from the teacher. A mother may be equally concerned when the child's whole conversation seems to be of school and his standards seem to be those that exist in the school and are set forth by the teacher. There is ground here, therefore, for a kind of parental worry that needs some resolution if the child is going to become comfortable in the new arena of learning activity.

The children who do best in the school situation are those in whom a sense of trust has been established in the early years and a lack of sense of shame in the later years of the preschool period. When this has occurred, the conflicts that the child has in changing his loyalties, adapting to his peers, and tackling with industry the problem of learning are close to nonexistent. When problems do exist, it is still possible to help parents to change, if they can recognize that their feeling of separation is based on a longing for the sole control over their child. Even the mother who has inadequately prepared her child by keeping him close to her and overprotecting him can learn through these schooling experiences that it is possible to give up one's child during a part of the day and still have him during another part. Openly facing the conflict makes it possible for the parent to gradually allow her child to participate with others and to accept instruction from others.

Parental Ambivalence to Peer Culture. Certain parents are equally concerned by the peer situation. We have noted that the child has steadily, from the end of the second year on, been forming groups and associating with larger numbers of children. In the school-age period this becomes more dramatic, since the child establishes a peer culture as a substitute for certain family activities. Many parents are concerned that their children seem no longer interested in family activities but prefer instead the strength and feeling of companionship that flow from the "gang."

Once more, one sees the difference in the sexes in this area. The boy's building of gang activities is usually much more frequent and intense than a girl's. It is not surprising, therefore, that parents begin to have a sense of being left out in the thinking, fantasies, and actions of their children. Again the parent, if he has not already learned it, must face the reality that the child's life is going to expand and that this is a part of normally becoming an adult. He is gaining independence, and there are assets in the outside situation that the family cannot give. It would take the very largest of families to offer to any child the range of support of his peers, and it would be rare that even in so large a family such support could be gained without the pulling and tugging of sibling rivalry which is a normal aspect of family living. Therefore, it is important to point out to parents the normalcy of the gang, the value of the peer support, and the comfort that the child can draw from this new kind of relationship.

Parental Ambivalence to the Child's Fantasy. The third area where the child seems to be slipping away from the parent lies in the expanded and changed use of his fantasies. Whereas the fantasy of the small child concerned itself with his body and its function, in the larger child the conflict between himself and the adult world becomes important. Thus, we see the particular fantasy of the Superman, an age-old phenomenon expressed in legend from Goliath or the Norse Gods or the denizens of Olympus down through the present space fantasies. The child seeks in his own way to compensate for the fact that he is small, that his rivalrous feelings against adults cannot conquer in reality but have to be taken into a world of fantasy. Literature, as well as all of the modern visual arts, has always supported this. A portion of it is normal and comfortable for the child; but when the child becomes preoccupied with the aggressive aspects of this fantasy, the physician should be concerned. It may be the clue that points to an unhealthy and probably punitive relationship between child and parent.

Some parents' concern about the child being infatuated with such fantasy stems again from the fact that the parent senses the loss of the child. It is important to remind such parents once more that they are eventually going to lose their children but that the loss need not be an abrupt, painful, nor dramatic event. It is more important to see that the child accomplish growth away from the parent in a piecemeal fashion and one that need not be grossly interfered with. Each child should be permitted his share of this fantasy in order to conquer the deeper feelings of concern, resentment, and antagonism that he has against being small. When this can be done in a partial fashion, the child can work through these feelings and come out with a sense of growth that will, in itself, be supported by his own development by the end of this early school period.

Psychologically, this period has been called the latency period, primarily because the child does not demonstrate during this period the overt sexual interests characteristic of the preschool years and that will flower again during adolescence. It is, however, not entirely a latent period, but rather a period when the child is pulling his resources together, learning how to work, and learning how to be a part of a larger society. The parents must, therefore, give him the opportunity for separation, for building peer contacts, and for working out some of his more immediate problems concerning size through the various fantasies that literature and the visual arts afford.

The job for the parents may well involve cooperation with the school and other outside agencies to channel the child's learning. The wider the range of the child's reading and artistic perceptions, the easier can he handle the necessary shift from fantasy to reality.

12

THE ADOLESCENT YEARS

The onset of growth that marks the beginning of puberty leaves in its train a series of living situations that make for what appears to be the stormy period of adolescence. In the child himself, growth is not an unmixed blessing. The once well-balanced smaller child must once more go through a cycle of learning—how to use his body, how to adapt it to his needs, and how to make an appearance before the eyes of others. The awkwardness of adolescence is an intricate combination of changes in muscle and joint activities, as well as the changes in perception that accompany any gross change in growth. What is more, the young adolescent becomes quickly sensitized to the changes in his body, and the awkwardness that results is correspondingly enhanced with each sensation of having done something crudely or out of place.

Secondly, growth at this particular phase in the life cycle is accompanied by a very massive growth of the sexual apparatus. This is no simple growth phase. The physiological and psychological concomitants of sexual growth are much more dramatic than any other phase of bodily increase. The pleasurable sensations of sexuality which have been present throughout the early stages of the child's growth now become focused and fused in true genitality. The equipment for adult life is present. Permission to use this apparatus is, however, not present.

With the onset of the earliest stages of puberty, society begins to take a hand in the developmental process. The simplest and most benign aspect of this new approach to the child is in the comforting words that the mother can use in preparing her daughter for the menarche. With such positive action it becomes possible for a girl to embark on this change in her living pattern with some comfort and ease. It is notable that this is not always so well done as it could be and that this leads at times to certain difficulties. But when it is properly carried out, it is a positive aspect of the parents' approach to the maturation of the child.

Not all of the forces of society, however, are organized in such a positive fashion. Lacking a tribal ritual and a manner of designating children as having changed from childhood to adulthood, our society has generally protracted the adolescent period and has set up a series of control mechanisms which remind one very accurately of the control measures used in the independent surge of the second year. Even before he attains any measure of sexual maturity, the child begins to feel the organized impact of society that will dictate the manner in which he shall live, behave, and act throughout the teen decade. A variety of controls, some of which Josselyn has called "temporal chastity belts," are set up in the form of rules concerning contacts with the opposite sex, times of leaving parties, etc.

It is obviously difficult for parents to set these controls consistently because our society does not have a universally accepted set of rules for behavior. The child, therefore, finds that there are many sets of standards for teenage behavior. Many of them are based on the concern of the parent lest the child misuse his new growth, his size, and his libidinous strivings. In varying degrees, parents communicate to children their great concerns over the potential of having adult sex relations. They are worried lest the children carry out the role for which they are physiologically being prepared.

A major differential in the growth of girls and boys further

Fig. 12-1. The earliest approaches toward members of the opposite sex are anxious and tentative, but necessary.

complicates this period. Girls have their growth activities one to two years ahead of the boys, so they reach a period of stabilization before their male peers. This discrepancy causes many problems in the relation between the two sexes and complicates the existing vagaries of growth for each separate sex.

It is not surprising that the child, during his teenage period, feels that he is a target for the scorn, the concern, and the control of all generations that have preceded him. That there is a very real "conflict of generations," as Pearson has pointed out, relates not only to parental concerns about the child himself, but those concerns deriving from the parents' memories of their own progress in this same period of life. For many of us adults, the years of adolescence were stormy and turbulent. Since it is not comfortable to remember these years, we swing powerful forces into action against our children. At times even our pity for them is turned to scorn and laughter as we mimic their awkwardness and make fun of their lack of personal and internal control.

This internal control of the child is modified by a further important dynamic. His growth recapitulates a period of earlier growth and inspires a reinstitution of parental controls. His sexual strivings stir up once more those sexual feelings which were present around the age of five when he was forced to make a decision in his relation to mother and father. The increase of sexual capacity not only rearouses this struggle but potentiates it in a way that the child could not enjoy when he was younger. Such a potentiation leaves the child in a position quite unlike that of his early experience. Now he is as big as his parents and has capacities which they know to be comparable to their own. Depending upon the way the child has handled the earlier struggle, the onset of this new power may arouse a gamut of feelings ranging from fear to a strong desire to rebel or to want to break out of the parental control in which he has been nurtured. Another very important aspect of psychological growth during adolescence is the shift the teenager must make in relationship from his parents to his peer group in early adolescence, and to members of the opposite sex in later adolescence. This shift is a momentous one involving a very significant redistribution of love and interest and a reappraisal of the self. In making such a shift it is necessary for the teenager to redefine who he is in relation to prior, current, and future relationships and roles. This conflict within the individual leads to some of the extreme variabilities of actions and emotions that are so characteristic of the teenage period.

The outsider watching these children becomes greatly impressed that the calm and evenly proceeding younger child has suddenly been caught up in a storm. The storm is manifested by a kind of a jerky activity in all spheres. Just as his motor coordination leads to awkwardness, so there is an awkwardness in expression and an awkwardness in emotional reaction. One moment the child is at peace with the world, and the next moment he is extremely angry; one moment the child feels comfortable and happy, and the very next moment he is plunged into the gloom of despair.

Out of this intense conflictual emotional striving, strong drives are born which are manifested in the attachment to the variety of social groupings. Here we see the dramatic espousal of religious faith. We also see the clinging to any other ideology that offers a stable base and a base which implies action. The child at this period, pushed from within by strivings and desires and controlled from without by the hedgings of society, must act. Such action can take place in a physical sphere, but it can easily take place in an intellectual sphere. The sports of this period, when properly controlled and adapted to the maturity of the muscular system, provide a healthy and desirable outlet for much of this conflictual striving. Society does not provide an adequate athletic outlet, however, for all children. These others, then, may turn to intellectual strivings and searchings with the same kind of drive reflecting the desire that burns within them. It is not surprising that they attach themselves to a host of dramatic ideologies which promise action as well as reactions. They suggest, by their very being, change and usefulness for the drive. The gang of the boy's latency period becomes a club with a purpose and an organization into which the child can pour his excessive energies.

It is equally apparent that any adult-sponsored organization

Fig. 12-2. The child is seeking to learn something about himself.

may fail in the effort to make a child feel that he is a part of it and that he is doing something for himself. Operating subtly, adults can offer children any kind of ideology, theory, or concept which will stir up and utilize the spark that is part of this adolescent conflict. When adults, in their zeal to channel adolescent activities, dominate youth organizations, they may find the children either rebelling openly or avoiding the group. Failure of this sort merely widens the gap between generations.

During this whole period the healthy child finds great comfort in his peers who are going through the same struggle. Rather than being derided for his awkwardness or his pimply face, the child can feel comfortable with other children and exploit to the full the variations in his emotional tone and his physical activity. One sees, therefore, a surging of power that not only enhances the best in the activity of youth, but emboldens them to seek other ways of approaching society—at times with the feeling of "getting even with" society. It is not surprising that delinquency, born out of the child's quest for something within himself and a feeling of reaction against those who would forbid it, flowers in this particular period.

On the positive side, Erikson points out that during this period the child is seeking once more to learn something about himself. Thus, as in his earliest sexual experiences of the preschool years when he was trying to establish the shape and use of his body, he tries to establish the totality of his body, his mind, and his spirit in the quest for identity in society. Here again the masculine and feminine roles must be redefined. In addition, the job roles must have a definition. Our society does not make any of these identifications easy. Because of the difficulty of establishing identity, many of the by-products of this age seem antisocial, or at least not geared to the society in which the rest of us live. These pressures in the child lead him to extremes and excesses. Changeability from abstinence to excess characterizes all of the actions and reactions of the child. In his food habits once more we see the excesses that were characteristic of the insatiable greed of the infant. The omnipotent selfishness of that early period is demon-

strated along with both the sloppiness and the concern about dirt
that was characteristic of the second year of life.

A particularly important aspect of this period is the use of the
self as a sexual object. We have noted that masturbation begins
early in life merely as a pleasurable experience, and later as a
rather frustrating activity in the preschool child learning about
his body. With the onset of adolescence and the flowering of a

Fig. 12-3. Pressures in the child lead him to extremes and excesses.

new physiological libido, the act of masturbation becomes pronounced. Present in the peer group is a variety of instructors who urge the child to try out the masturbatory activities. But early in life the child learned that masturbation has connotations which were to be feared. The age-old condemnation of this practice, based on society's concept of the procreative function, has led the child both to fear and to worry about its activity. Yet the drive within him enforces a desire to carry it out.

It is not surprising, therefore, that a major flood of guilt surrounds the child in his masturbatory activity. This guilt enhances and makes more striking the discomfort the child feels in his association with his elders. This guilt becomes a part of the fantasies that accompany the act. Many children feel that they are being spied upon, that people are aware that they are masturbating, and that they are known, as well as doomed, for the practice. The pleasure is accompanied by fear. In extreme examples this becomes an outstanding symptom in the psychoses which are characteristic of this stage of life. Prohibited from overt sexual activity by the demands of society, the child turns to personal sex activity and finds himself running into his own superego as a manifestation of the conflict that he carries within his own mind.

The resolution of these conflicts is not an easy process. Once more, what has happened to the child earlier makes it possible for him to solve and resolve the identity crisis. But there must be available some opportunity to establish identity, and wherever this is true the child prospers. Where identity as an individual, as a member of one's sex, and as a contributing member of society is lacking, trouble occurs. The child may then make a delinquent identity.

Education provides once more a notable area of possibility for help. Most children at this period of life are able to sustain themselves away from their family, to enjoy the intellectual and physical activities that are a part of the schooling process, and to gain from it some concept of how they can use their own talents. Lucky the child who can see, and be helped to see, those areas of his own capacity that can be fully used as an adult.

Physicians are particularly well suited to helping a child see himself. This is especially true if, over the years, a good rapport has existed. Because so many of the youth's concerns are with his or her body, the physician is presented with emotional problems disguised as bodily complaints. In general such children should be seen alone, as individuals. Their clinical complaints should be seriously received and adequately explored. The physician is then in a position to look behind the complaint for signs of emotional discomfort, for the groping toward a sense of "who and what am I," and for a real longing for a sensible adult with whom to talk. Children quickly sense our value judgments but will also easily confide in us if they feel that we know the problems of this age period and are not going to condemn them merely for being adolescents. The use of neutrality, coupled with clinical knowledge, is the greatest asset available to us in working with this age group.

13

THE ADOLESCENT YEARS: PARENTS' ROLE

In discussing the teenager we used the concept of the conflict of generations. A part of this conflict is born out of a major feeling of helplessness on the part of the parent. While it is true that the image which the adolescent presents stirs up memories of this period, it is also true that some of the feelings of unease come from the fact that the parent feels there is very little he can do for the child of this age. His own memories of the period suggest a time of storm or feeling of inadequacy in trying to go through these years. The adult remembers how awkward and concerned he was. The father remembers his tentative gropings in the sexual sphere; he remembers his attempts to get dates and the feeling that he would be scorned. The mother remembers her concern lest she be considered a wallflower, or an equal concern lest she be considered too popular. In all instances, the parents' memories are those which concern the vagaries of this period. It is not surprising that many parents themselves have memories of how poorly their own parents handled the situation. From such memories come feelings that they must try to do better by their child as well as questions as to what can be done.

The child's increasing size may be a source of internal distress to him, but it is a source of concern equally to the parent who feels that his control is slipping away and that he can no longer handle the young giant that stands before him. Equally, the parents are concerned about the sexual attractiveness of their girls and have great fears lest something occur that will dramatically modify this attractiveness. The personal control that parents felt over their young children because they were smaller and, therefore, could be mastered is threatened by the very fact of growth. The addition of the sexual component makes it doubly difficult. Parents are barraged daily with tales of sexual intimacy among children varying from mild flirtations to overt rape. Each parent has a very natural concern about the fate of his child and a very real interest in prolonging maturation so that the child may be happily and successfully married at the end of the adolescent period. No parent wishes his or her child to plunge too quickly into adult sexual activity. All of this is compounded by the child's stimulated intense interest in sexuality. Lay literature, once more in this century, has become more overtly sexual. Pornography pervades the offerings of the communications media. These are realistic concerns and compound those that stem from the newly aroused sexual desires of the parent as he sees sexual interest flowing anew in his child.

We have noted earlier that children tend to break away from the home with the onset of school and form themselves into small groups or gangs. In discussing the adolescent, it becomes apparent that these gangs take on much more significance and have a greater meaning than they had when the child was younger. Whereas a younger gang was primarily focused on sports and simple activities, the gang of the teenager can become a focus for intellectual, social, or spiritual life. It is not again surprising that parents feel that this is a much greater threat than the activities which took the smaller child away from home. Here the parent sees someone else, be it peer or youth leader, changing the mind of the adolescent, and he has some concern about such a role since he feels replaced. Parents approach this problem very differently of course, and, whereas we see some parents very actively ridding themselves of their children, we see others that are overly concerned that their children are being wrested away from them. The mean between these various behaviors suggests a normal interest in the child's learning new things and the parents' tolerance of the ability of the child to move out of the home. This norm, however, is rarely seen, and the physician is confronted either with the parents who tend to cling too closely to their child or with those who abandon the child to the tutelage of others.

There are two major areas in which the parent can still be of considerable help to the child. One has to do with the general matter of discipline. It becomes apparent from what we have said before that disciplinary control over the child at this age is merely an extension of the manner in which the parents have handled the earlier disciplinary problems. The parent who is truly respected by his child need have no concern about disciplinary activity at this age. If the parent can be helped to accommodate to the fact that the child is growing out of the home, is going to establish new contacts, and may even set up some new thought processes, he need not be concerned so long as the child retains a respect for him as a parent. But the parent who has continually fought with his child, usually from the age of two upwards, is quite likely to sense major difficulty at this age because of the overt possibility of rebellion. The preventive aspects are quite obvious, but it is still possible for parents and children to develop a more tolerant attitude toward one another. While much of the assistance that the physician can offer applies directly to the parents during all the early stages of growth, the young adolescent is a talking and responding being who can participate in the new family approach. The pediatrician, who can at this stage talk with both parents and child and often with the whole group together, can accomplish much. (We will discuss later the possibility of talking to the adolescent as an independent individual, another important approach to these problems.)

Probably the best way to handle the problem of discipline is to make it open and mutually agreed upon in all areas. The situation then becomes not one of parental control of the child nor the child's rebellion against the parent, but rather some mutual understanding of what is and what is not tolerable. This knowledge may lead to respect on both sides. It is usually true that when children have grown up not respecting their parents, there is a lack of respect on the part of the parent for the child, for his capabilities, and for his possibilities.

The other major area in which the parent becomes involved with the child concerns attitudes towards sexuality. We have already mentioned that the mother has a simple and easily positive job in helping her daughter establish her menarche. This can be done without fear or concern. The girl moves easily into this very normal physiological process and goes on from there with comfort in her bodily processes. Where the mother is prudish or fearful of talking about sexuality, the child buries her concern, only to have it erupt later in pains and difficulties of menstruation.

The same process for the boy is not so simple or clear. In general, boys have rapidly picked up some smatterings of sexual knowledge from their peers. They learn to masturbate, and they become puzzled over the occurrence of nocturnal emissions. Therefore, the role of the father (and here it must be father rather than mother) tends to have a retrospective therapeutic role rather than a preventive one. It is very difficult to talk about the boy's problems in advance of their occurring, and it is nearly always necessary for the boy to have had some sort of sexual experiences or sexual conversations before the father can sit down and try to clarify the situation. Such clarification is often a simple way of assisting the boy. It avoids the heavy-handed, "Now it is time to talk about the birds and the bees," problem that faces many fathers. If a father can approach the situation by trying to find out what the child knows about sex and then clarify it with him, he can perform a very useful function. Very often it is necessary for the physician to get this process started. It seems best, however, that the physician not do this entirely by himself, but perhaps in a three-way conversation among father, son, and doctor.

One clinical area not frequently considered has to do with the overall control of adults over children merely by virtue of being adults. It certainly has nothing to do with bigness, size, or muscular ability. We are all aware that we do have controls over them that are at times fantastic. Young patients tell us that they can hardly wait until their eighteenth birthday to break away from the family. In these incipient rebellions one is struck by the fact that there is nothing to stop them breaking away from the family at any time except some simple financial control. More important, however, is an intangible hold that the parent has over the child. This has been built into a legal situation, yet the child is unaware of the source of this control. What is important is that this can be used for good as well as for evil. Parents who continually threaten and abuse their children with legal, financial, and other intangible controls, breed nothing but rebellion. Parents who, however, utilize the fact that their mature state in life does give them a hold over the child can turn this same hold into a comfortable attitude of direction which the child is still happy to have. Just as we saw younger children who were fumbling for a knowledge of themselves and found it good when the parent set limits on them, so we see the same process in adolescence. The normal search for identity that the adolescent is undergoing is often in need of boundaries, limitations, and controls. When they can be supplied with some judiciousness and not merely to spite the child or to compensate for the parents' concern, they have some validity. When, with the help of the physician, such controls can be thought through and made reasonable, the child respects them, respects the source, and gradually becomes amenable to the kinds of limitations that are necessary and valuable.

These are the positive controls that the parent can have during this period. Much of the time we find ourselves cautioning parents not to do certain things that they are doing. It is well to have available certain positive pieces of advice that are based on reason, thought, and an appreciation of the mutual stages of both parent and child. While it is true that for some parents a major job is accomplished by merely getting them to "lay-off" their children, for others the offering of a positive substitute for irrational behavior becomes extremely important.

Irrationality can be subjected to certain simple tests. One has to do with whether the action of the parent stems out of fear. This fear can be a concern about the child's activity, or it can be a fear of what the parent will do to the child should the child get into difficulty. Parents who have multiple and frequent temper displays are probably acting in fear and panic whether their child is doing right or wrong. Irrationality can also be tested against extremes. Certain parents are extremely liberal, others extremely conservative in the manner that they handle their children. Wherever one sees chronicity in these extremes, one can suspect that a certain irrational approach is being carried out; and difficulties arise from such irrationalities.

More important, parents can present to their children a valuable ideal for identification merely by demonstrating a good marriage. Parents who mutually respect each other offer the best evidence that adulthood is worthwhile and something to strive for. Such an image is more valuable than any manufactured contact with children. The truth of this is so simple that it should not be belabored. The attainment is often, unfortunately, difficult.

PART III

ABNORMAL DEVELOPMENT

14

RECOGNITION OF ABNORMAL BEHAVIOR

There have been enough hints in the earlier part of this book to suggest that abnormal or deviant behavior lies very close to normal development. It is, at times, very confusing for the observer to separate what is abnormal and should elicit concern from what is well within the normal range. As we have already stated in Part II, we believe that a knowledge of normal development of the child, with an understanding of the tasks characteristic for each age period, will prove invaluable for appraisal of a problem. Deviant psychological functioning can then be understood as a distortion, exaggeration, or diminution of normal processes. Such changes in the normal developmental pattern may occur acutely and cause high parental anxiety, or they may develop slowly over a long period of time. A presentation of a seemingly acute situation may illustrate the diagnostic process:

Pete, a bright but quietly observant four-year-old, was the second of four children, the youngest of whom was eight months old. The mother, having brought the youngest child for well-baby care, had established a good medical relationship over a long period of time in the care of her children. But then she stated that Pete had developed a peculiar blinking of his eyes ever since he had had the "flu" two months previously. Pete had previously impressed us as an alert, intelligent, friendly boy. He had not demonstrated any serious psychological problem, although earlier the mother had reported that he had wanted to have babies when she was pregnant. This desire appeared to be a positive expression of his wish to be identified with his mother, a wish to which he was rightfully entitled at the age of three, since she had provided his main anchorage to the environment. The acute illness he had experienced apparently was mild, but Pete resented having to stay in bed since he was a notably active child. Observation confirmed the mother's description of a strange blinking of the eyes, and further inquiry revealed that it had first occurred on the day when his mother told him he could not go out to play and would have to stay in bed.

Comment. In such a situation one can think of a variety of causes for such a symptom, but to clarify this situation, further history was elicited. The history suggested that, in addition to the tic, Pete's appetite had diminished, he had not slept so well as formerly, and he seemed to mope around. He asked many questions about the baby. This mother was not notably over-solicitous of her child's health. It was obvious that Pete would resent having to stay in the house, but the symptom of eye-blinking suggested more than a mere expression of immediate resentment. Physical examination indicated that his general recovery from the flu was adequate, and that there was nothing wrong with his eyes. The clue of his anxiety about the baby suggested that his symptoms may very well have been related to the common situation of rivalry following the coming of a new intruder to take his place in his mother's affection.

His specific symptom, however, of blinking of his eyes suggested a further possibility; namely, that there was something that he had done and did not wish to look at.

In this case, as in many similar situations encountered in pediatric practice, one does not have the opportunity to actually trace the origin of such a symptom but must be led by what is known already of normal psychological development of children during this age. A common source of short-lived symptoms in childhood during this age is identification; the child takes on for himself certain behaviors, attitudes, and feelings that he observes in others with whom he has a close emotional tie. Identification with the aggressor as described by Anna Freud is a very common form of identification seen in aggressive little boys who are frightened of their aggressive fathers. In the case cited above, the child's wish to have a baby was a form of identification with the mother, with whom he had a close tie.

Such a sequence of clues suggests that the solution of such a simple problem is not met merely by reassuring the parents. The boy does have something wrong with him, and a simple reassurance that it will go away is not totally adequate. The mother's anxiety concerning the problem must be discussed. Some explanation of the boy's fear must be given to her so that she can focus more attention on relieving him. If possible, the boy can be led to talk about his new sister and his mother, either to the physician or to the mother herself. Inasmuch as he is entering a stage of life when his concern about his relationship with his father becomes equally important, it would be valuable to talk with the father in order to improve his relationship with the child.

We are not often confronted with such acute emotional problems; rather, parents usually bring situations to us when they have become more fully developed. Except with very young children, parents tend to delay mentioning to the physician their concern about any symptom or group of symptoms. Thus, it is more common that we are presented with a series of complaints relative to an emotional disorder that has been going on for some time. It is true that parents need a period of observation in order to convince themselves that there is a pattern to the child's problem, but it is also true that they are hesitant to bring it to the attention of a physician. For a parent to come complaining that she cannot control her child, that he is anxious and restless in school, that he is a source of concern to the teachers, is somehow an admission of her own failure. The embarrassment and shame make her delay the process of calling the difficulty to the attention of the physician.

Therefore, we must use as criteria for seriousness certain other guidelines. The *first* has already been mentioned—namely, the *chronicity of a process.* This is true whether it has been continuing for months or for years. The fact that any one symptom has persisted over a long period of time gives it greater value and highlights the fact that the child is in need of care for a psychologic disturbance. *Second,* the *intensity of the situation* relative to other aspects of living is important. The child who is occasionally rebellious and lashes out at either parents or teachers is not worthy of such intensive study as the child who consistently rebels. When a pattern becomes set within the child and normal developmental progress does not occur, then there is a very real need to think about intervention and psychiatric evaluation. *Third, is the number of symptoms.* Studies have shown that mere cataloguing of the number of symptoms relates to the intensity of the internal conflict and serves as an expression of the need for psychiatric or psychologic help. *Fourth, the manner in which a parent describes* the symptomatology of the child is important. The parent who pours out a hoard of venom as she describes the symptoms of the child is probably describing a serious situation, even though she may not mention at all her own relationship to the problem. Equally, a parent who is overly bland and describes the child's behavior in a totally objective fashion should lead one to have particular concern about the nature of the relationship between parent and child.

These four categories serve as the guidelines for looking at any problem, be it acute or chronic, in trying to determine whether or not it is a situation that warrants further investigation of the behavioral situation.

15

DEVELOPMENT OF ABNORMAL BEHAVIOR

Throughout the earlier part of the book we have described the child's behavior and personality pattern as a sum of many inter-reactions between his growth and his environment. A variety of handicapping conditions can complicate a child's growth, some of which are discussed in detail in a separate chapter concerning the handicapped child. Children with abnormal motor function develop in unusual manners, and the reaction of the parents to them is complicated both by their feeling of concern for the child's progress and their feeling of their own responsibility in the causation of the illness.

Some children, however, demonstrating no overt physical disabilities are yet the products of abnormalities, occurring either in utero or at the time of birth, which leave them with a condition variously described as "neurological handicap" or "minimal brain damage." The evaluation of such disturbances is only now becoming organized. It is apparent from such studies that certain of these children present themselves to their parents in a manner that makes the ordinary caretaking more difficult.

John, age four, was characterized by the mother as a very hard child to handle. Birth had been prolonged and difficult, and there had been a moderate delay in the child's taking his first breath. Physical examination and a detailed neurological examination, however, revealed no abnormalities. The child generally ate well but slept poorly, was frequently irritable and never seemed to be quite satisfied with his general care.

The leads that seem most valuable in assessing the development of these children suggest that the minimal amount of brain damage interferes both with subtle motor function and with visual perception. It may well be, as we come to learn more about it, that the perceptual difficulty of these children is the most important. It may be the thing that alters the child's concept of how he is being cared for and leads in turn to the irritability. This has its own consequence, because as a mother is faced with an irritable, crying, unhappy child, she finds it more difficult to carry out her normal maternal functions. Many of the psychophysiologic disturbances of the first year may fall into this category.

An unfortunate outcome of such a disturbance is that parents whose capacities make handling a child difficult under the best of circumstances find these children much more disturbing and are prone to become irritable and annoyed with them. This irritation leads at times to an intensive search for a neurological component to the child's abnormality; a search which may serve as an excuse for the mother's difficulty in caring for the child.

This is an important and subtle phenomenon to which many physicians become a party. It is not easy for any of us to accept responsibility for somebody else's difficulty. One of the major problems in preventive work with children lies in the fact that we must at times point out to parents that they are either in error or seem to be mismanaging their part of the care of the child. In a reaction to such seeming criticism, the parent becomes stubborn, obstinate, and reluctant to accept the responsibility. One way to avoid this responsibility is to turn toward a diagnosis that seems not to involve the parent, namely, the neurological handicap. Parents seem to grope for the diagnosis of "brain damage" in order that they may feel that something is wrong with *the child* while *their care* itself is quite adequate.

Thus, we see in parents' attitudes toward psychological disturbances in their children a spectrum of possibilities, of which the two poles are often outstanding. On the one hand, the child's disorder, behavior, or development is ascribed to malfunctioning of the child in the same sense that a car functions or does not. At the other pole the parent considers it entirely due to his own neglect or imagines psychic injury. Some parents seem to relish the guilt that goes along with their mishandling of the child; other parents avoid the guilt by the most extreme measures.

A bright, physically and neurologically normal, seven-year-old was referred for psychiatric consultation because of setting fire; poking other children in the rear with his index finger and instigating others to do the same; drawing pictures of women with large penises; and tyrannizing others to the extent that they were afraid to speak up against him lest he beat them up. The father, a scientist, while truly concerned about his son's disturbing behavior and wishing to have it alleviated by whatever means possible, felt extremely pessimistic about the outlook because he believed that all behavior and all mental phenomena could be explained in terms of tissue changes, or enzymatic or biochemical events.

In contrast, another case is Herbert. He was an extremely bright eight-year-old boy referred for consultation because of persistent bedwetting and because his mother feared he would do physical damage to his brother during their many battles for possession of cherished objects or during "games." She stated, "I was terrible to Herbert as an infant and I know that it was all my fault. I treated him mean and was always yelling at him and wouldn't let him do things." When asked for details she could only recall that he was a very active boy and extremely curious, and she used to get angry and tell him to stop whatever he was doing. In a similar way she blamed herself for her husband's philandering and nonsupport.

The same two attitudinal poles are often seen in a physician's rigid insistence either upon a hereditary transmission of personality traits and characteristics or that "a child is the product of his environment." We have illustrated in the earlier part of the book the great impact of environment on the child. It is very important to remember that regardless of the background of the child, the most modifiable part of his development relates to the human environment in which he grows.

It is, therefore, important to recognize that neither of the opposing views is appropriate in fully explaining the complexities of a child's psychological disturbance. What, then, are some of the specific ways in which the parents contribute to the child's deviant development or psychological disturbance? The first and most obvious of these is the situation in which the parents actually traumatize the child. This word is often loosely used, but certain chronic relationships with children serve as examples of such an etiology. In early infancy a lack of sensory stimulation is perhaps one of the most serious traumas that an infant can experience. We will describe this in greater detail under the concept of *deprivation*. It is equally important to recognize that many parents, in their efforts to handle a child, overstimulate such children. This can be equally traumatic. Overfrustration, as in teasing or rejecting mannerisms that thwart children's early needs persistently and over a long period of time, especially in the presence of overstimulation, is another chronic trauma.

One of the commonest of the traumas of childhood is over-gratification. Earlier we discussed the "spoiled child" and described him as one who is protected from experiencing every type of frustration as perceived by the parent. The child is not allowed to clearly experience his own unmet needs. He comes, therefore, to anticipate that everyone will gratify him. He fails to adapt himself to the varying requirements of an external role and to know his own instinctual processes and become comfortable with them. Such children have great difficulty in distinguishing between reality of life and the fantasied magic of existence.

Other traumatic experiences for children in their development include such things as inconsistent or erratic reactions on the part of the parents to the child's behavior and to the requirements of his care.

An older boy whom we saw had his early life complicated by the untimely death of his father. The mother poured what she thought was an abundance of attention upon him. She tried to make up for the loss of father by anticipating every need, by smothering him with attention. In doing so, however, she felt at times that the child was a great burden because she had been deprived of her husband's support. This sense of burden caused her to become angry at the slightest deviation of behavior even though she had promoted many of the child's reactions. The combination of overstimulation and overprotection, a defense for not truly wanting the child, led him to become quiet, unresponsive, and extremely obstinate. One of his outstanding obstinacies was a failure to do well in school, which was not at all in keeping with his good intellect.

Social stimulation is an extremely important part of a normal child's development. The fact that children are played with and the fact that a family laughs as well as cries provides an atmosphere of cohesiveness which makes the child appreciate the realities of growing up in a family setting.

In the example noted above, the mother was given to periods of considerable depression. At these times she felt the burden of loss of her husband most keenly. During such periods the overt reaction that she normally displayed was traded for an avoidance and encouragement of the child to carry on alone. Lacking the normal modes of carrying on, the child could only sit unresponsively, staring at the ceiling, a fact which provoked the mother further when she thought of the misuse of his excellent brain.

It is also important to realize that even within the same family no two children grow up in the same environment. A series of interconnected events modify the role of the parents towards subsequent children. First children conventionally feel that they are the testing ground on which the parent works out his emotional reactions. Indeed, first children are often either overprotected or overpunished; but subsequent children, also, may suffer either by inattention or by a feeling on the part of the parent that ignores the child's progress since it seems unnecessary always to be looking at him. More important, certain children within a family become "selected" for difficulty:

A three-year-old boy was already exhibiting markedly disturbed behavior toward other children. His two brothers and a younger sister, age twelve months, had none of the difficulties that bothered this child. Outstandingly, the child had been born at a time of considerable family stress. During his first year he had been a quiet, passive child and was essentially neglected by the mother, who was focusing on the care of the older children and trying to shore up her relationship with her husband. During the second year, however, the family situation improved but the child reacted by being demanding and aggressive. Such attitudes were not well appreciated by the parents, and the child received much more punishment than his preceding siblings. A product of these difficulties began to appear when the child first made poor contact with other children in a nursery school setting.

Finally, each parent, as he rears his child, recapitulates the history of his own upbringing with that of his children. Different aspects of this upbringing may be revived with each child. The struggle of the parent with the instinctual life of the child is especially pertinent to this recapitulation. Examples of this will appear in later chapters.

16

THE FIRST YEAR

Our emphasis on the initial approach of the mother to her child suggests that observation of this process may well give clues of potential trouble as far as the subsequent handling of the child is concerned. Particularly, one should be alert to the mother who has great difficulty in establishing a comfortable early relationship with her child. There may be certain aspects of the child's appearance or behavior that concern her, yet she may be loath to talk about it. The mother who is grossly uncomfortable in the lying-in situation warrants clinical intervention in order to clarify what it is in the care of the child that so bothers her.

Many mothers, particularly with first children, have a considerable fear of the child. They are concerned lest it break or be damaged by something that they do to it. We mentioned earlier that mothers are greatly concerned about the intactness of their children. This demands a kind of a reassurance that can best be given during a thorough examination by the physician. When this is done in the presence of the mother, it can be much more comforting than merely telling her later. This may well be an important technical step in the doctor-mother relationship.

Pathological behavior in infants is demonstrated chiefly by

abnormalities of physiologic activity. Since the actions of the child tend at first to be diffuse and relatively unorganized, the child manifests his emotional discomfort, as well as his physical discomfort, in terms of simple physiologic functions. Signs of pleasure or displeasure are obvious, but these affects are most often called to medical attention by disturbances of function. As feeding, sleeping, and elimination make up the bulk of the responses of the child at this time, it is not surprising that the early manifestations of emotional disturbance appear in these three areas. Of these, probably the most common is that of colic.

COLIC

Colic has a long and dramatic history. No better description of colic has been written than that of Thomas Phaer in his book published in 1544, one of the first textbooks of pediatrics in the English language. More recently, however, observation of colic has focused not only on the agonal difficulty of the bowel but on the fact that the infant appears to be in a state of widespread physiologic distress. One author has pointed out that the child is unhappy all over. Not only does there appear to be a disturbance in the gastrointestinal tract, but the child is in agony, his muscles are drawn up, he cries incessantly, he will not be comforted, and, in general, he paints a picture of global distress.

The widespread aspect of this difficulty has led current authors to describe this condition as "excessive crying in infancy." The fact that in many instances this crying seems to be definitely part of a daily cycle, particularly late in the day or early at night, lends further support to the idea that much colic results from expressions of anxiety on the part of the mother in handling the child and the child's reaction to this. Classically, this illness does occur at a time when the household is upset. Instead of the placid daytime care which the mother offers, the husband has arrived home and adds to the activities of the house. The mother may well become anxious, both in keeping the child quiet and in satisfying her husband. This continues on into the evening.

It is not surprising, then, that colic tends to be a nocturnal phenomenon, coming at a time when parents are tired, when interaction is increased, and when the ordinary calm care that can be given to a child is lacking. Characteristically, also, efforts on the part of the anxious mother or father to handle the child seem to be met with increasing defeat. As the parent becomes more concerned and anxious about the manner of handling the child, the child responds by a forced and urgent expression of unhappiness so that it has become standard for the child to be described as one who cries and cannot be comforted. The cumulative tension-building aspect of this illness is characteristic of many subsequent anxiety states and sets a pattern for the difficulties that can occur in the relationship between a mother and her child.

What is equally characteristic of the histories given by these parents is their vivid description of the colicky process and their expressions of concern about the child. It is much less common to have a mother talk about her own anxieties, her own frustrations and inabilities, and finally her own anger at the distress her child is undergoing. Recent studies, however, have suggested that one of the important phases in treatment lies in getting the parents to talk about their own concerns, their guilts about the handling of the child, and particularly their very real anger against the child and often against the marital partner. Since many mothers are left to cope with this situation by themselves, they feel both defeated and deprived. Such an admission by the mother leads to an outpouring of feeling and quite often to a recognition of an individual role in the fostering and perpetuation of the disturbed interpersonal relations in the colicky process:

A young mother, harried and distressed about her child, consulted us concerning a severe colicky situation which was keeping her awake most of the night trying to feed her crying four-week-old baby. The wife of a graduate student, she lived in a student housing project. Her husband, absorbed in his work, gave relatively little time or attention to the child and, in fact, thought that it was her responsibility. The baby's crying, irritability and distress had increased over the past ten days most noticeably from about 10:00 p.m. to 2:00 a.m. The mother expressed great concern about her child, but only when she was able to talk about how annoying it was to her, how little help her husband had been, and how greatly she wished not to be burdened with this problem, were we able to gain a complete picture of an anxiety-provoking situation.

The physician who tries to cope with colic merely by readjusting the formula finds that he is forced into doing something else by way of consoling, reassuring, and talking with the parent. More important is the opportunity for such a parent to give vent to her true feelings about the situation in order that she can be relieved of this seemingly perpetual anxiety. When the hostility towards the child can be brought out into the open, it is amazing what relief can occur and what improvement in handling methods may result. It is sometimes possible to assist such a parent by a demonstration of handling methods if one has available a conscientious and able nurse. This is particularly valuable if the nurse can go to the home at the time when the colic is occurring and assist the parent in the actual management. Lacking this, however, the most important single item seems to be the opportunity for the parent to talk about her own relationships with the child, the meaning of her worry and concern, the burden it puts upon her, and the subsequent anger she feels at having been made to bear this burden.

OTHER FEEDING PROBLEMS

Many other complaints referrable to the feeding situation are brought to the physician. Further in this chapter we will discuss the difficulties ascribed to constipation. Loose stools may also indicate either poor maternal care or an excess of anxiety on the part of the mother about the manner in which she is carrying out the feeding. Many mothers become overburdened with anxiety because of the desire to carry out patterns of child care popularly prescribed in books on child-rearing. To be helpful to such mothers requires more than mere medical skill in the appraisal of the child or parent's distress.

It is important at this point to assess one's own feelings about the manner in which parents are to handle their children. Breast-feeding is an outstanding example. Many mothers, anxious to breast-feed their children, find major difficulty in carrying out the process. At times they feel that they are bucking the combined efforts of their friends, their husbands, and their relatives to carry through a process which should be simple and normal. In their extremity they turn to the physician. It is important to recognize that as physicians we have feelings, some of which are derived from clinical knowledge and some of which relate to our past or our cultural upbringing. Breast-feeding, then, may be seen unconsciously as a rather degrading or primitive way of child-rearing. The physician's feelings may be complicated by the fact that he feels he can do a better job of nutrition than can the mother.

It is beyond the scope of this book to discuss the variety of feelings which a physician can have about a natural phenomenon of this sort. Nonetheless, such feelings permeate our advice. In advising or trying to assist a mother who is struggling with the process of breast-feeding, it is important not only to know the simplified methods of assisting her in the process, but also to have a concept of all that is involved. The physician who feels that this or that mother is not going to go through with breast-feeding turns against her in his own efforts to help. This is truly a situation where it is as important to understand one's own feelings about motherhood and mothers and babies as it is to understand the complexities of the whole feeding situation.

Subsequent feeding difficulties during this year usually relate to specific foods. Aside from certain known allergic situations, many infants present a pattern of finicky eating or refusal to certain foods. For a long time physicians have been acutely aware of the consistency in patterns between mother and child in such refusal and finicky behavior. Mothers, when quickly challenged as to whether they disliked the food in question, respond with an openness about their own feelings which is often therapeutically helpful. They are little aware of the disdainful manner in which they offer such foods.

It then becomes the role of the physician to deflect their interest, concern, and, at times, displeasure away from the specific food item to the manner in which they are offering foods. Certain mothers lack the capacity to offer a range of food. It can be pointed out to them that once a balanced diet is obtained the range of food is not particularly important. Many women feed children a variety of things merely because it is urged by neighbors or, worse still, by enterprising salesmen in the stores. To reassure them that a plain, simple, but nutritionally adequate diet is all that the child desires is profoundly important. To teach mothers the simple methods of offering foods so that they don't present them as something unpleasant is a helpful educational task that can lead to the avoidance of many food idiosyncrasies later on.

Some parents make a tremendous effort during infancy to stuff children. The importance of this act lies in the fact that such stuffing can lead to an active rebellion on the part of the child in subsequent years. Whenever this symptom is demonstrated, it calls for great tact but also great firmness in suppressing it.

SLEEP

A second major area where physiologic disturbance can be observed is in variations of sleep patterns. The normal sleep of the child is long during the early days and only gradually diminishes to some twelve to fourteen hours by the end of the first year. Aside from gross sleep reversal patterns which seem to occur in certain families, most children sleep comfortably during the early months of life. These reversals of sleep pattern are difficult to understand, and one must investigate the sleeping habits of the family in order to see whether or not some gross aberration of sleeping on the part of the family may not lead to a confused picture of sleep on the part of the child.

More important, however, is a rather specific response which occurs roughly between the seventh and ninth month. At that time, many children who have previously been good sleepers develop a wakeful pattern, often at the most inconvenient hours in the middle of the night. A full explanation for such wakefulness is not readily available. As we pointed out in an earlier chapter, during the second half of the year children become aware that they are somewhat different and distinct from the mother and are aware of a separation from her. It is possible that the anxiety attendant on such separation may lead to disturbed sleep, either through dreams or through manifest symptoms.

At any rate, the child tends to awaken somewhat frightened and crying and in need of some comforting kind of care from the parents. It is notable that this disturbance occurs more frequently when the children are kept in the same room with the parent than it does in those who are placed in their own rooms with a definitive schedule. The syndrome also occurs more frequently where the mother is generally anxious and concerned about the manner of rearing her child.

In its simplest form, this situation is usually met quite promptly by the mother who comforts the baby by offering it either food or reassurance and places it back in bed. After a few nights of this experience the child apparently becomes adjusted to the nearness and comfort of the parent, and the symptom disappears. On some occasions, however, this becomes a serious matter. The mother who is anxious about her child and who has concern or guilt about the manner in which she is handling him, responds to the child's demonstration with an increased concern that is readily communicated to him by the manner in which she cares for him.

Thus, rather than offering comfort to the child, such a parent stirs up and makes more uncomfortable the small infant. The infant responds by crying, by being excessively agitated, and by refusing to go to sleep. A pattern similar to the earlier colic is built up. In severe instances, this crying pattern may go on for hours or even may continue for days, with the whole family becoming not only more anxious but more agitated, angry, and ineffective in their care. In such severe instances it may be necessary to take the child temporarily from the parent and place him either in a hospital or in the hands of a capable nurse. More often, however, the pediatrician himself can be comfortably reassuring that the illness is a time-limited one, that the parents' anxiety can be expected to change, and that the important ingredient is to meet each particular session with a calmness based on understanding.

In those instances where such general reassurance is of no avail, it becomes important to initiate, at this particular point, a closer study of the child and parent and their relationship. Every effort is needed to get the mother to talk out her concerns, whether they are resentment against her husband, annoyance over the burden of care, or anxieties related to situations completely outside the problem of care of the child. The importance of this particular symptom lies not in its temporal occurrence, but in the fact that the handling of it demonstrates clearly the manner in which the mother will handle similar situations in the future. While it is true that this particular pattern rarely persists, the simple expedient of telling the mother that the child will "grow out of it" is not adequate. More important is a clear discussion of the mother's immediate role in the handling of her child and the meaning of this role in relationship to the rest of her life. A simple inquiry into the manner in which she cares for the child, her feelings about it, and the general state of her marriage and child-rearing situation may be quite helpful.

ELIMINATION

Two phenomena relative to the child's physiologic response seem to have more cultural determinants than personal ones. There is a group of patients that feels very concerned about bowels, bowel habits, and the manner in which the child eliminates. In many of these instances, the complaint of constipation appears early. Usually, examination of this situation suggests: (1) that the child is not in any way constipated, but is not having stools frequently enough to satisfy the parents; and, (2) that the parent herself is constipated, often a family tradition for generations. It is impossible to alter and modify such cultural attitudes quickly. However, an explanation of what can be expected and an explanation of the tolerance of children for retaining stools can often assist mothers who are under terrific pressure from their families and neighbors to get the child to produce a stool at intervals suggested by laxative ads rather than by childhood necessity.

TEETHING

The same is true of teething patterns. As we suggested earlier, many children grow up and erupt their teeth without any indication of pain or difficulty. In certain families, however, it seems culturally important to have teething difficulties. Again, one cannot buck culture, but teething can be handled with a minimum of concern on the part of the physician. Offering the ordinary comfort that can be given by simple medications and understanding may suffice to assist mothers through this period. Excessive medical zeal may exaggerate the value of the parents' complaints and lead to further distress.

PARENTAL EFFECT ON CHILD'S DEVELOPMENT

Finally, all that we have said during the discussion of normal development suggests that the physician must be concerned about the effect of the parent on the developmental process. Wherever his observations suggest that parents are putting too much pressure on the child to speed up his development, a gentle and often humorous discouragement of such efforts can be made. Equally important, where neglect or deprivation of the normal personal relationships that are a part of the developmental process is discovered, interference on the part of a physician is mandatory.

All of the observations of development suggest that the child needs the normal stimulating activities of ordinary child-rearing. The simple handling relative to feeding, playing with the child, the changing and cleansing him, all offer a normal amount of comfortable stimulation which makes development possible. When this does not occur and when it becomes apparent that the mother or father is grossly neglecting the child, it becomes incumbent upon the physician to search for ways in which this can be rectified. This usually cannot be done in one or even in a few sessions. The baby care practiced by most pediatricians gives an opportunity for a continuing review and a continuing opportunity to make suggestions as to the amount of attention the child should have. In circumstances where such care seems to be lacking, the repetitive contact with the parent and child serves as a very valuable vehicle for the communication of mutually satisfying child-rearing concepts and for the education of the parent in carrying them out.

In considering the developmental advice to be offered to mothers during this period, it is necessary to recognize that every aspect of care provides an opportunity to establish relationships which can be supportive to the child as well as to the parent. The satisfaction for the parent is fully as crucial as the care offered the child.

We have already suggested that the child's response to caretaking may be demonstrated in both pleasurable affects and unpleasurable conditions manifested by physiologic and general disturbances. Skin rashes, excessive respiratory distress, diarrhea, vomiting, constipation, colic, disturbed sleep—all these may be ascribed to physical causes at times, but each of these symptoms may serve equally as a warning signal that something is awry in the mother-child or parent-child relationship. The opportunities to intervene are more frequent during this year because parents seek medical advice more freely at this time.

A child who had been followed from birth began at the age of about two months to demonstrate a change in feeding patterns. Originally content, the child began to be extremely fussy and picky about her foods, and the parent who was attempting to introduce solid foods felt frustrated and concerned. At this two-month visit the mother was unable to pinpoint any environmental difficulty or change that might cause the disturbance. The child looked perfectly healthy and was seemingly content, but the mother stated that she cried every time strangers came into the home. At the time of the third-month visit the child's irritability was more marked. While her gain in general had been adequate, she had been more vacillating in her acceptance of new foods. At this time the mother was able to talk about the manner in which her mother-in-law consistently and constantly advised her concerning the child's feeding. In general, this advice contrasted considerably to that given by the physician. The mother would not have been anxious about this had not her husband sided with the mother-in-law and begun to deride her. An attempt was made at this visit both to understand the situation and to reenforce the simple diet which the physician was offering. By the time of her sixth-month visit the situation was more severe. The problem was concerned no longer with eating but with a general feeling that the mother was inadequate and unable to care for her child. The child was showing increasing irritability, and the mother pointed out that it was hard for her to pick the child up, yet the child cried so constantly that it seemed increasingly necessary. It was apparent that the home situation was getting more difficult.

By special arrangement, a visit with the father was arranged. He proved to be not so adamant or difficult as the mother had described him. Other factors relating to their earlier married life were beginning to complicate their relationship, but it had not gotten to the point of a mutual distrust. The father felt complimented by the physician's interest in him. Both parents were able to discuss openly their difficulty in the presence of the physician. The father had felt estranged from the care of the baby by the mother's possessiveness, which she ascribed to a fear of the mother-in-law's taking over. An open evaluation of these problems led to an opportunity to change the general pattern of the care of the child. Due to failed appointments, the child was not seen again until eleven months of age. At this time development had continued to be normal but there were still periods of fussiness and irritability. However, parental relationships had considerably modified, and the father had felt strengthened by his contact with the physician in a way that led him to support his wife, to contradict his own mother, and to correct partially some of the ways of handling of the child. It was felt that continued contact could be useful but that a distressing and potentially dangerous disturbance in family relationships had been aborted by the contact with all members of the family.

17

THE SECOND YEAR

Either from lack of recognition or from embarrassment about presenting certain problems, parents tend not to consult a physician for emotional difficulties that arise during the second year. Our preliminary material on development suggests that this is an extremely crucial year in setting a pattern of relationships between parents and their children. Not only does the child have all of the tasks of learning, but the parents begin to initiate their controlling activities during this period usually in relationship to the actual progress of the child. Thus, there is very often an unfulfilled opportunity to guide parents in the manner in which they set up the controls and express their feelings of discipline, punishment, and so forth.

THE OVERPROTECTIVE PARENT

It appears that the physician's task in this year is divided into three common patterns of relationship. The first pattern is the overprotective, overanxious mother whose anxiety about every step that the child takes makes her prone to do too many things for him, to protect him in too many ways, and not to offer him independence. Such an attitude will nearly always be demonstrated during the first year, but the child's opportunity to be independent is, of course, considerably less. Therefore, it behooves the physician who has had an opportunity to follow such a child to watch for those areas in which the mother is not taking advantage of the child's learning or progress and to encourage her in any manner at his disposal to permit the child to do more for himself.

Particularly, he should be aware that such a mother is very likely not to permit a child to feed himself and learn the use of utensils. Equally, she will be very dilatory in expecting some activity on the part of the child relative to dressing. The same mother may be quite urgent about speech or even toilet training but will tend to take over and do things for the child when he should be learning to do them for himself. Such a mother needs much encouragement and pushing in order to get her to permit the child to have some expression of his own.

It may be necessary to discuss with her why she is so loath to permit the child any independence. Usually, this will be found to relate to some fear or anxiety lest the child harm himself. Such anxiety stems from the very common fact of guilt, relative to something the mother did or did not do very early in the child's life. She is worried lest the child get into difficulty and blames herself in advance for what might happen. It is not easy to counsel such a mother, particularly in relationship to the freedom she allows the child to wander about the house or yard. However, it is possible to bring her to a more realistic outlook and to set up proper safeguards so that the child does not get into danger. She may then permit the child to have as wide a range of activity as possible within these controls. At this stage a child is comfortable if he can be permitted to range as widely as possible within a somewhat controlled area where help and support can be given by adults.

THE OVERDEMANDING PARENT

The second and equally common pattern of relationship that the physician must deal with is seen in the parent who, during this particular period of time, is extremely pushy with his child. He compares his child with every other child. He makes special demands in intellectual areas and is particularly concerned about the gaining of speech; therefore, he puts a heavy emphasis on the child's verbal ability. Assisting a parent with this particular phase of growth calls for some understanding of the speed at which the particular child is going. The physician who has kept a moderately accurate tabulation of the child's progress will be in a good position to predict what the child may next be expected to do. If the parents are demanding behavior well beyond that of which the child is capable, there will be very good reason to point out to them clearly and distinctly the kinds of difficulty they will be causing and the trouble that the child will be getting into. Such children become frightened, timid, and anxious about their progress. In the verbal area the child may begin to clutter up his words in the haste to get them out; a mild form of stuttering may thus occur. The child may be anxious about cleanliness because of the pressures to conform to toilet habits of an older child. All of these things breed anxiety in the child, and the anxiety turns to other kinds of acting-out difficulties as the child grows older.

THE OVERPUNITIVE PARENT

The third pattern of potential parent-child conflict is seen in those instances when parents are demonstratively punitive. It is not easy for the physician to set the moral tone of a family, but his allegiance to the child will very often cause him to be concerned about the manner in which parents carry out their discipline. Discipline is important, and controls are necessary for every child, but cruel and harsh punishment is not necessary to achieve this end. Many parents who will listen to no one else will take very frank talk from a physician.

It is not always easy to observe this pattern, because parents are not prone to bring such problems to the attention of the physician. The physician's nurse, however, may be well aware of some heavy-handed activity in the waiting room, and it is possible to build up quickly a picture of harshness and cruelty demonstrated in the community. Whenever it is possible to talk with such parents, it is important to do so, since from the punishment and discipline of this period is set the pattern by which the child will relate to the parents. Under heavy punishment some children become extremely submissive and apathetic and are soon lacking in motivation. The parent who complains when the child is eight that he will not learn in school, may be paying the price for some heavy-handed activity when the child was attempting to learn.

The converse, of course, is the child who rebels openly and actively and develops a classic acting-out behavior pattern with rebellion starting at this time. Such patterns can be very consistent: they will cause trouble to the child in his peer and school relations; they will cause difficulty for him as an adolescent and an adult. Whenever, therefore, the physician has an opportunity to modify the kind of punishment that a child is getting, he will do both parents and children a massive service that would otherwise take tremendous amounts of undoing when the child is older.

TOILET TRAINING

We have stressed the learning problems in this particular year. It is important to realize that the potential of the child is modified in a very complex fashion. The emphasis that the parent puts on the toilet training process may bring out a variety of parental motivations. On the one hand, there may be concern about cleanliness; on another, about morality; and, on a third, there may be the very real need to control and dominate the child. Such active interference on the part of the parent breeds very different responses on the part of the child. The child responds to the attitudes expressed; and since, from his point of view, he is merely carrying out a normal process of learning and self-expression, it is not easy for him to understand the enormous value placed on this simple process.

Because of this intense value, children learn either to fear the act of defecation, to express their hostility by using their feces and smearing them around, or to resign and become apathetic about the entire act. The moral tone that parents impute to this process sets another pattern of fear that becomes built into the child's growing conscience and may lead him to distort many other values in his learning. For these reasons the psychiatrist, looking at this process retrospectively, has great concern as to the manner and attitude expressed while the act is being carried out. Anything that can be done to assist parents to approach learning and training in this particular area with a relatively calm and rational point of view will redound to the benefit of the child and make him more comfortable as he proceeds into later stages of both learning and of parental relationships.

Examples of situations encountered in this age period follow:

Elaine, age four, a child with psychogenic megacolon, an attractive, winning little girl, always wished for her parents to wipe her bottom. This request had its origin in their insistence on keeping her clean even before the development of the symptom of withholding. For Elaine, it was a sign of love and a way of keeping her parents close to her when, indeed, she felt quite remote due to the defects in the general nature of their relationship with her and the estrangement which they felt with her.

Walter, a six-year-old, partially blind, autistic boy, when entering any new situation would immediately rush to the bathroom and flush the toilet. He also had the habit of stacking all the waste-baskets in the house in the bathroom, and especially taking the wastebasket from his parents' room and placing it in the toilet bowl. His mother was perplexed by this behavior, but in speaking with her it was learned that the closest relationship which she had with Walter earlier was in relationship to toilet training. She would sit with him, holding his hands while he had a bowel movement, talking with him and generally being affectionate and reassuring. His toilet-flushing ritual and his wastebasket ritual could be understood as transitional phenomena, the way of insuring the presence of the parents, or, in this case, a substitute for that parent who would relieve anxiety through closeness at the toilet. In this case, too, there was a serious estrangement between the child and his parent, with murderous wishes on the part of the parent. The child understood this, and responded to them with frightening self-destructive activities such as running out into the street when the mother would leave the car door open.

Richard, a three-year-old boy, seemed quite unhappy when his parents took him on a visit to relatives, and in this setting got in the habit of calling his mother early in the morning to come and wipe his bottom. It was an urgent, plaintive cry, insistent but not desperate, full of affect rather than ritual. Richard's mother, an aggressive, vigorous, but affectionate woman, was amused and a little annoyed but complied with his request.

Barbara, a bright four-and-one-half-year-old girl, outgoing, affectionate, loving, and appropriately conforming in most ways but not all ways, awakened at night crying and was always relieved when taken to the bathroom by her mother. She was afraid of messing in the bed and would always go to sleep smiling after her return from the bathroom.

Comment. In each of the above instances, it is apparent that a symptom of behavior in some way related to anal activities and the bowel functioning has been used by the child and by the parent as an expression and a remnant of the struggles the child had undergone in his relationship with the parent who had trained him. In understanding the outcome in each instance, it is important to consider two factors:

The first factor is the general quality of the child's relation with the parents. In the case of Barbara and Richard, the quality of this relationship was sufficiently healthy to guard the child against serious pathology. In the case of Walter and Elaine, the quality of this relationship was deficient to the extent of leaving the child unprotected in a potentially traumatic situation. In all instances, the traumatic situation here was the child's own overwhelmingly strong impuses for anal gratifications. In the two pathological instances, the symptoms indicating pathology were of a specifically anal character.

The second important factor concerns the details of the way in which the parent handles the specific maturational task that the child is called upon to master, that is, the task of achieving cleanliness. The way in which the parent participated in this helping relationship determined the nature of the symptom which expressed the general disturbance in the relationship between the child and the parent. Thus, we can understand that two factors weighed one against the other and related one to the other determined the nature of the outcome.

A healthy relationship between a child and the parents is to some extent insurance against the development of a pathological symptom. The details of how the parents handle the child's maturational tasks determine the nature of the symptom that expresses the child's struggle with himself and the parent. The symptom will, however, not necessarily develop. Another point illustrated by these cases is the fact that behavior such as the illustrated may represent either (1) the child's defensive efforts with his own instinctual forces and his repetition of attempts to regain the lost parent who helps him deal with those forces, or (2) an adaptive device in helping the child meet situations in his environment. Such behavior can also be utilized as an alarm to indicate to the parent the need for something special; thus, it is a communicative device as well as a symptom expressing internal conflict.

Another factor that influences the outcome of such behaviors is the inherent strength of the child's ego. A weakened ego is particularly vulnerable to stress from within or without since the character of the ego is determined by the history of the child's relationship to external need-gratifying objects, i.e., parents. Strength of ego likewise depends upon the general qualities of the child's relationship with those parents during early formative months and years.

18

THE PRESCHOOL YEARS

It is uncommon for parents to bring their preschool children to the physician because of emotional difficulties unless the disturbance is a major and dramatic one such as severe withdrawal and bizarre behavior as would be seen in childhood psychosis; persisting nightmares; unsuccessful bowel training; or evidence of serious developmental retardation. The subtler forms of neurotic disturbance, personality deviation, or misbehavior, are generally regarded by the parent as part of the child's normal struggles during this age. The criteria to determine which is an expression of a normal struggle and which is an indication of a significant problem in development are discussed in Chap. 14.

SEPARATION ANXIETY

A major task for the child during the preschool period is to be able to enter social situations away from his familiar home and function without the help and reassurance of his mother. When the young preschooler is able to make a successful adjustment to nursery school, everyone usually gives a sigh of relief, acknowledging the fact that the child has been successful in accomplishing this task. In some cases, the sigh of relief is a bit premature because some pseudoindependent youngsters may, at first glance, appear to make the break but with minor stress, such as a new teacher, an aggressive child in the group, or a minor illness or injury, regress more readily than would be expected. The child who shows some evidence of struggle in leaving the parent and appears gradually to master it is generally in better psychological shape than a pseudoindependent youngster.

The clinging, anxious behavior of some small children when exposed to the outside world usually indicates maternal over-protection, oversolicitousness, or overconcern in the earlier years. Much of the effort toward changing this symptomatology must, therefore, be focused on understanding the attitudes of the mother. It is important to discover why she feels the need to overprotect or hang onto the child. In most instances, this is related to some early concern that she had about herself in relation to the child. Certain children become particularly precious because of special circumstances. After a series of miscarriages, the product of a successful birth may come to represent another threatened loss to be worried about and overprotected. Likewise, a child born following the loss of a sibling or any sort of death in the family may take on undue significance. Sometimes a male child of divorced parents carries the burden of consoling the mother or father. To allow the parent to express her guilt and worry about this child early, to look for ways that she can let the child go rather than hedge him in, becomes an important task for the physician if withdrawn, fearful, behavior of the child is to be prevented.

SEXUAL CURIOSITY

A second major area of anxiety that parents may express, either incidentally or as part of a larger problem, concerns the child's curiosity and interest in sex. In Chaps. 8 and 9 we have already discussed the fact that children explore themselves and enjoy exploring others. In this period, then, there is likely to be a con-siderable amount of tentative masturbation and a good deal of sex play between children. The manner in which parents handle this matter is of considerable importance. While it is not to be condoned, neither is it to be forceably and roughly condemned. The physician's job in helping the parents feel their way through this stage will depend on his ability to provide an interview situation in which the parent may talk out his or her own feelings about the problems. Particularly, the physician must be concerned with those parents who seem to be overly emphatic in their punishment of the child, inasmuch as it overly stresses the importance of these particular explorations. The parent who is cruel or punitive or sets undue value on punishing such a child only stirs up the child's curiosity and makes him more excited about the interest which he has discovered. This may lead to further difficulty later on.

Parents may encounter questions from the child that they feel cannot be answered within the limited vocabulary and conceptual ability of a child. In such instances, a partial and general answer may be given with the promise of further information when the child has learned more and grown up a little more.

It is important, also, to bear in mind that parents who feel especially anxious or poorly equipped to deal with questions and behavior of their children regarding sexual matters are usually unsettled in their own minds regarding these questions. Such parents often "overeducate" or overstimulate their children regarding sexual matters. Such overstimulation is expressed by the child in frequent and overt sexual experimentation and exhibitionism. In such instances, it may be helpful to address oneself to sexual education of the parents rather than the child. Such parents should be encouraged to restrain their impulses to exhibit, educate, and demonstrate.

Specific inquiries should be made in such cases into parental patterns regarding bathroom and bedroom privacy. They should be helped to understand the need for privacy and modesty in sexual matters. Such practices as undressing in front of the children, bathing with the children, leaving the bedroom doors and bathroom doors open and parading about the house in the nude should be discouraged. Sleeping with children and examining the child's buttocks and genitals should also be discouraged. All such behavior on the part of the parent (mother *or* father) arouses excessive anxiety in the child and makes it difficult for him to master normal sexual tensions. Children can govern much more easily feelings aroused by spontaneous sexual exploration of each other than those aroused by that between children and adults. Such interchanges between child and adult leave the child frustrated because the mother or father unconsciously stimulates him sexually and makes sexual demands upon him of which both child and parent are consciously unaware and stir up more than the usual amount of fantasy.

This unawareness makes the problem difficult to deal with. The physician must be both discreet and forceful in making every effort have such behavior between child and adult discontinued. Should the attraction continue, it could become more serious, leading to major pathological difficulties in the child's sexual identity or becoming, via fantasy, the nucleus of a neurosis or perversion. If it can be noted and prevented at this particular time, the physician will have achieved much. Very often this close relation is presented by the parent as a complaint about the child such as nightmares, tearful anxiety, sexual acting-out behavior, or bed-wetting.

When Peter was four, his mother stated that she felt he was reacting badly to nursery school. He seemed not to enter into activities, and the mother felt that this was a carry-over because his sleep was restless. For some months now he had been awakening at night and coming to her room. Of late, she had accepted him in her bed, her husband being frequently away on business. This led to stormy night-time scenes during the weekends when the father was home.

Comment. Two separate problems are apparent. One is embodied in the concerns of the child, who found difficulty in leaving the mother to go to school. The other is that of the mother, who felt abandoned when her husband left. A firm statement explaining the difficulties of continuing this nighttime relation seemed to relieve both parties. It was then possible to approach the individual fears of mother and child and to give support to each toward a goal of mutual independence.

SPEECH DIFFICULTIES

When the child is learning to organize his speech and words, the effort may be so extremely difficult that a simple form of stuttering, often called cluttering, becomes evident. Whenever this is observed, one can look for some sort of pressure by the parents, in relation either to general behavior or, in particular, to the verbal product. It is not enough merely to remonstrate with these parents about such pressures. It is necessary to talk with them about the difficulty they will face in giving up such pressure. This type of parent does not give up easily, and considerable work may be necessary with them by someone in order that they lose this need to hurry the child along.

TICS

As with so many symptoms, tics, in the form of eye-blinking, face-twitching, head-jerking, facial contortions, and postural movements of various types, may reflect identifiable stress in the child's relation to the family, the struggle with his own instinctual (sexual and aggressive) impulses, or both. When tics persist for more than a few weeks, it usually is a signal of significant inner turmoil in the child and should be regarded seriously. Specific inquiries should be made about other family members or other children who may have similar disturbances, since children often take on the nonadaptive behavior of others with whom they have a close but conflictual emotional tie.

Ben, age four, had been an outstanding nursery school student. His drawings were imaginative, clever, and well done. His ability to draw, however, began disintegrating when eye-blinking began. The blinking was rather excessive, involving both eyelids, and was accompanied by sniffing movements of the nose and a twitch of the mouth. If he were a little older and had developed this symptom, one could have anticipated trouble reading.

His father, an engineer, was very busy and his mother felt deserted by him and became depressed. In consultation it was apparent that her depression was not solely related to her husband's unavailability. She developed some symptoms which included eye-blinking and other movements and twitches of her face and body. As a result of her depression, this boy's relationship with the mother became more tenuous and he experienced loss of her love. He developed the same symptoms his mother had. In this way he did not have to give her up; he had her right within him. He could do just what she was doing, and in his mind this meant that he had his mother with him again, an attempt at restitution. Consultation with the parents resulted in some correction of the father's absences from home. This helped the situation. The mother remained depressed, however. Later she entered psychoanalytic treatment; and as she improved, so, also, did the boy's symptoms disappear. Follow-up two years later showed that Ben was doing well in school and had no further neurotic symptoms.

DISCIPLINE

Many parents complain about disciplinary problems with children in this age period. Fortunately, at this stage it is easier to trace the origin of such difficulties in the concerns that the parents themselves have about punishing, controlling, and assisting the child. It is a frequent observation in medical practice that many parents today are extremely afraid of their children. So concerned are they about inflicting harm on them, that they refrain from the ordinary kinds of controls that the child needs to limit the excesses of his behavior. To learn how to control himself, the child needs limitations; yet many parents, fearful of causing harm, refrain from putting limitations but subsequently turn about and punish or otherwise excessively control the child in a belated attempt to correct their own permissiveness. Fortunate, indeed, is the physician who has an opportunity to talk with parents about the disciplinary problems of this particular age period. The parent can be given some sense of his own worth and possibilities; excessive temper reactions can be talked out and understood; and a real opportunity to set guidelines for the child can be made at this particular period.

Dwight, a bright five-year-old of divorced, intelligent parents, lived with his lonely mother who had trouble sending him to bed at a reasonable hour. He wished to have his mother with him. His mother only increased his anxiety at bedtime by her elaborated and prolonged attempts at reassurance. It turned out that it was the mother who was afraid of being alone in the apartment without a husband. Only when she could firmly and consistently insist on a regular bedtime did Dwight reveal that he had carried on previously as a way of making his mother do what he wanted her to. Success in such manipulative tactics with his mother then really made him anxious. After all, if mother was so frightened that she had to go into such prolonged and elaborate explanations, Dwight really should have something to worry about. Parental guilt and anxiety are the child's most powerful allies in his battle for omnipotence over his parents.

RUNNING AWAY

One manifestation of the child's extreme rebellion and feelings of loss is the symptom of running away. Many children do this occasionally in order to demonstrate their own confidence and self-satisfaction in their ability to be independent. Chronic running away, however, is serious. In this age period it suggests rather marked interpersonal difficulties that need careful understanding and investigation. It is not sufficient, in such an instance, merely to talk with the parent loosely about punishment and controls; underlying difficulties that have led the child to take so drastic and rebellious a step must be discussed. Running away is often the child's attempt to find something he feels is missing at home. The child that begins to run away early and continues to do so regularly warrants more serious investigation than the primary physician is able to give. Psychiatric referral of such a child is clearly indicated.

ENURESIS

One is not alarmed about the child who continues to wet the bed after the second or third year; but if he reaches his fourth birthday without nocturnal control, it is well to consider it abnormal. Certainly, if it persists beyond this point, it becomes dignified by the name "enuresis" and is considered a symptom of some importance.

Enuresis is one of the oldest known disorders of man. It has been subject to a variety of concepts of etiology as well as to a gamut of therapeutic procedures that almost surpasses the human imagination. At the present time, psychological causes are considered the most important in most instances. Whenever other sources of difficulty have been ruled out, the child who persists in wetting the bed must be considered to be in some sort of a conflictual situation, either with the home and parents or with his own internal wishes, and is expressing this difficulty in the symptom of bed-wetting. The symptom gathers intensity because its initial simplicity is complicated by the fact that sheets are wet, the room becomes redolent with ammonia, mattresses are damaged, parents' tempers become exaggerated, and a whole cycle of bad relations between child and family are initiated.

Parents resort to many methods of handling this symptom, mostly of a highly punitive nature. When simple punishment fails, some desperate parents begin to use the shame and embarrassment of sending the child to school with a note to tell the entire class that he has wet the bed once more. Handling such situations demands first an investigation and then certain moderate efforts to control the symptom within the range of ordinary medical care. In this particular symptom complex, it is important to remember that there are disturbed relationships between child and parents and that both child and parents must be taken into account in the handling of it. It is not enough merely to advise the parent to let up on the punitive measures which he or she is utilizing or to limit fluids at bedtime. It is equally important to have the child's participation and understanding of the way the physician understands the symptom in order to effect a beginning in therapy. Seeing the child and parents separately may reveal a not inconsiderable struggle between them, part of which the child seems to be handling by the destructive act of nighttime wetting. Therefore, it becomes important to secure the child's cooperation, to get his willingness to change and to try to understand, if possible, what the strife is about within the family. Unfortunately, the symptom may persist in many instances even after such clarification and opening up of the family situation. In such instances, it is apparent that the deeper unconscious problems that plague such children and are represented by this symptom may already be in action. In such instances, more prolonged psychiatric care may be necessary and a referral may be in order.

Billy, a bright, handsome, but sensitive boy of ten, had achieved urinary control day and night at age two. At age three, following the birth of a brother, he began night wetting, which continued, despite limitations of fluid at bedtime and being taken to the toilet in the middle of the night. His longest dry period had been for one month, three years prior to referral. Other difficulties included "a persecution complex," the feeling that no one liked him. He often said, "I wish I were dead," and "I can't do anything." He was felt to be "mentally lazy" by his father. His mother thought he was like his father and the father's sister, both of whom were said to be "mentally unstable."

In this case the symptom of bed-wetting was understood as arising out of his rivalry with his brother and his wishing to regain the favored position of the infant in the family. The bed-wetting might have cleared up had the normal rivalry problems been successfully resolved. However, the attitudes of both parents toward the symptom and the use of Billy as a focus for their own marital differences kept the symptom going, and Billy was left with the feeling of not being able to do anything. The tendency to cling to the infantile behavior was also fostered to some extent by an episode of poliomyelitis four years prior to referral which left mild paralysis. It seemed that the only way in which Billy could gain parental love and approval was through the bed-wetting.

Father and mother were seen in interviews jointly; and when marital differences were brought into the open, they were helped to see Billy's problem as separate from their own problem. Billy was seen for six visits once a week. He turned out to be a boy with some talent, as far as his verbal ability was concerned, and he illustrated in many excellent drawings of ships and automobiles his wish to move away from the center of the family difficulty. He discussed his fears during the time that he had polio and explored briefly a fear of spiders which was found related to his ambivalence toward his mother and her ambivalence toward him. After these interviews the bed-wetting cleared up, and his mood changed considerably with this achievement. His relationship with the doctor over this brief period allowed him to take a step forward in his independence, which was not possible with his parents alone. His mother, whom I had encouraged to return for further visits, declined since she was beginning to be faced with some feelings which she herself did not wish to recognize.

Follow-up of this boy seven years later at the age of seventeen showed that the symptom of bed-wetting had not returned. He had been doing well in a commercial art course in school and was now interested in cars and girls. His parents' marital difficulties continued, but Billy was no longer enmeshed in them.

Comment. This case illustrates the important point that a child's symptom may have its origin in early life but is maintained by neurotic interaction among family members and can be dealt with, sometimes rather briefly and directly, by an outside agent who is able to support the child in his growth and help the parents acknowledge the difference between the child's problem and their own.

BOWEL DIFFICULTIES

Either fecal soiling or withholding of bowel movements in a child four years of age or older is cause for concern by the parent and physician. A careful history often reveals bowel difficulty extending into the first and second year of life. Such difficulty may reflect disturbances at any level of psychosexual development. Correction of this problem is contingent upon the ability of the parent and the physician to forego interest in the child's bowel and address themselves, instead, to the child's total functioning and feeling state. A careful appraisal of the child's relationship with the parent is indicated. Most easily overlooked is the secret pleasure taken in symptoms by both the parent and the child. Other sources of pleasure and other forms of communication of child and parent must be substituted for the bowel-oriented relationship. Repeated anal examinations of any kind should be avoided. The use of enemata, suppositories, and cathartics should be completely abandoned. Too often in such cases both parent and physician become fellow collaborators in their investigation and "therapeutic" attention to the child's anus, stool, and bowel functioning, thus, only reinforcing the symptom and offering the child nothing in its place.

A four-year-old boy in psychiatric treatment, who had been successful in having bowel movements in the toilet by himself after a long history of withholding that led to psychogenic megacolon, was confronted by his mother's recurrent anxiety regarding his bowel habits, despite his improvement. He said to her, "Don't hurt my tooshe the doctors have fixed up."

The symptom of fecal soiling is most often associated with overflow incontinence, i.e., paradoxic obstipation. Occasionally, soiling may be seen in children who have, for various reasons, not been successfully trained and yet do not withhold their bowel movements. Other soiling children may do so under conditions of increased anxiety or at times when aggression and hostility is openly expressed. As with all symptoms, treatment should follow, not precede, an understanding of the symptoms.

19

THE SCHOOL YEARS

While the usual pediatric practice tends to focus on infants, psychiatric practice is heavily overloaded with children in the age range from six to twelve. Enough has already been said to suggest that the problems of these children do not necessarily arise at this period but may only become manifest. This may lead to efforts by the parent to do something. An important change, over and above his own adjustment difficulties, occurs in a child's life when he enters school. His parents have observed him either fondly or harshly, but with a certain amount of normal parental pride as well as a rather deep investment in what happens to him. However, an outside agency, such as the school, regards the child along with all other children and may make more objective determinations concerning his behavior, his progress, and his ability to assimilate himself into this larger world.

Thus, many children whose intellect is marginal prosper comfortably in their own family settings only to find themselves in real difficulty when they must face the task of learning imposed by the school system. Equally, children whose difficult behavior has been held in check by some punitive actions and reactions of the parents may find themselves uncomfortable in the school setting and quickly conflict with the authorities. Since almost all children attend a school in some fashion or other, their presence in school activates a screening device to reveal emotional difficulties, low intellectual potentials, or other evidences of failure or maturity or maladjustment in the developmental process.

Parents confronted with a concern by the school react in various fashions. Some express great anger at the school for having discovered something unusual about their child and come rushing to the physician full of antagonism and implications against the school system. Others become greatly embarrassed, as if the school had discovered a guilty secret. They, also, come in a state of great anxiety to the physician, hoping that the school can be proven wrong, the parents vindicated, and everything set right once more. It is in such circumstances that parents often present themselves for emergency consultation. The mere threat of dismissal from school becomes an instant source of anxiety to most parents, so imbued are we with the importance and value of the child's being a part of the normal educational setting.

Even in less acute situations, the fact that the child's behavior in school is a source of bother and concern to teachers and peers becomes transmitted back to the parents, and they become anxious about symptoms that were noticeable for a long time but were either denied or covered up.

PROBLEMS OF SEPARATION ANXIETY

We have already outlined the particular difficulties that the child faces in going to school, adjusting to the school, and learning. In discussing these difficulties, we mentioned the anxieties that erupt from the first cause and express themselves mostly in fears, panic reactions, nightmares, and school avoidance. The occurrence of abdominal pain, headache, and so forth, is classic in these children who have difficulty in separating from home and in entering school. Of chief importance in handling these early school problems and in handling the phobic reaction, is work with the parents. This must be designed to help the parent understand why she is clinging to the child and making it hard for him to separate from home. Most of these parents are quite unaware that they are doing this; therefore, much projection of the physician's interpretations will occur. However, the painful process that the child demonstrates in separating from the mother can itself be used to show the problem. Even with simple counseling, the mother can be encouraged, through support, to give up her child to the new people in the school setting and make an adequate adjustment which will assist the child. The more serious phobias may require more intensive treatment.

Repeated examinations of Susan, age eight, had convinced her physician that her complaints of abdominal pain had no base in organic pathology. Apparently, the mother accepted this diagnosis, for she was not seen for several months until the parents returned, stating that she refused to go to school. Again, she appeared healthy, despite an attendance record of increasing absences for "severe stomachache."

A check with the school revealed no academic problems, but a lengthy description of the daily tantrums and scenes whenever the mother tried to deposit her at the school entrance. The mother usually took her home and had recently seemed to give up the struggle.

The mother was full of complaints about the organization of the school and especially about the teachers. One sensed that she was protecting the child from what she felt to be dangerous outside forces. She was easily led to describe her own concerns at a similar age. Although she spoke of Susan clinging to her, the teacher had described the mother's wistfulness at those times when Susan had been persuaded to enter the building. The initial diagnostic contact with the school established a base for a firm stand that the child belonged back in her class. This became a positive prescription.

More difficult was the job of convincing the mother that the child could survive without her. Reassurance alone, without daily demonstration, would not have succeeded. A third step, that of separate interviews with the mother to permit her to explain, ventilate, and eventually understand her fears, led to a shift in her attitudes both to the school and the girl.

PROBLEMS OF ADAPTATION TO SCHOOL CULTURE

Children whose adjustment reactions are associated with difficulty in adjusting to the peer culture or the school setting itself, frequently demonstrate disruptive, aggressive behavior that is a major source of concern to the teacher. These are the children who are threatened with expulsion and whose parents are called in to hear the complaints and worries of the school. The physician confronted by a parent of such a child must first establish the reality of the situation. It becomes important to get a school report to assure both parents and the teacher that the physician is interested and will be a responsible member of a group trying to work out the problem. Very often such active interest on the part of all concerned ameliorates the immediate situation, and further diagnostic efforts can be made.

In such instances there is often a very clear and outspoken difficulty between parents and child which can be interpreted and understood only over a period of time. Children do not usually rebel openly or act out in their learning situation unless they are carrying over to it a struggle that is part and parcel of the home situation. It becomes then the responsibility of the physician to clarify this difficulty and to determine the severity of the situation. When the learning difficulty or school behavioral difficulty is accompanied by a great many parental complaints, it is obviously a severe situation that calls for referral and specialized treatment. It is possible, however, at times, for schools to manipulate the situation if it is early in its development by permitting the child to be placed in a more comfortable school classroom setting where he can operate more comfortably. Such manipulation is often valuable in the early stages of such a difficulty. It is unfortunate that such stages are rarely brought to the attention of the physician because of the normal concern and embarrassment of the patient.

PROBLEMS OF ACADEMIC LEARNING

Children who present special learning difficulties are usually screened out by the school system. At the present time many schools have psychological testing and counseling available, but it is sometimes important for the physician to intervene in order to emphasize certain defects in the child that make learning difficult and interfere with the normal process of education. In such instances the physician plays an extremely important role in clarifying the whole situation and bringing medical attention to bear on the psychological testing and the relationship of such testing to the child's behavior.

Of real import is the fact that failure in learning at the elementary school age is a very serious phenomenon. For various reasons, children tend to bear the difficulties of later learning much more easily than failure at this period.

The outcome of systematic failure on the part of the child during this particular period becomes clinically notable later on. It is in this period of time that a sense of achievement or failure is established by the child. This is particularly notable in the instance of learning to read. This accomplishment forms a base for much of later learning. When a child does not succeed in this task, he carries a special burden with him to succeeding academic experience. Because of this difficulty and the perpetuation of the sense of failure, anything that can be done for children at this particular age is of prime value. Physicians need to be especially alert to the kinds of anxieties that children demonstrate in order that remedial steps at this point can be taken before the child digs himself deeper into a rut of despair.

Remedies, however, depend on knowledge. We have described the expanding contacts of the child and the change this makes in older relationships. At this stage many of the preventive steps which the physician can take may be mediated through other professionals. To tackle a school problem without consultation with school authorities leaves the diagnostic problem incomplete and fails to use an important asset in either prevention or cure. It may well be that the physician becomes an administrator of various forces that impinge on the child's life. His continuing knowledge of the child and family makes him uniquely able in this role.

20

THE ADOLESCENT YEARS

The in-betweenness of adolescence is manifest not only in the feelings of the child but in the manner in which medical care is sought at this particular period. This ranges from the conventional childhood procedure, wherein the parents seek help for their child or bring the child with any sort of complaint, all the way to the child feeling in need of help for himself and seeking it on his own.

In addition, the kinds of things that bother the child become very different at this stage from the things that bother the parent. The latter is concerned about deviant behavior, conflict with the law, difficulties in school, and personal worries about the manner in which the child is growing up. The child is much more concerned with things intrinsic to himself: worries about his body, anxieties about masturbation and subsequent guilt, and all of the conflicts between himself and his peers of both sexes. This leads to quite varying symptom presentations. In general, whenever a parent comes in complaining about rebellious or acting-out behavior on the part of the child, the latter has a group of rejoinders. He protests about the manner in which his parents restrict him, confine him, lack understanding of him, and in general seem to stand in opposition to his total way of life.

The internal feelings of the child, be they represented by somatic symptoms or pure anxiety, are often kept tightly to himself. Very quickly children sense that their worries about their body, their face, their changes in size, and their awkwardness are not things to impart to adults. Just as they hide them from their parents and others, so they are often loath to express any of their true feelings even to a trusted physician. Fortunate, indeed, is the physician who has had an opportunity to follow a child for a long period of years and can be considered as someone detached from the family and, therefore, worthy of trust. To him the child will bring his worries about subjects as diverse as acne, on the one hand, or experimental sexuality, on the other.

Since it is culturally anticipated that the girl will need a reasonable amount of instruction relative to her menses, it is often easier to talk with a girl in this period than it is to a boy who is concerned about seminal emissions, masturbations, acne, or the stirrings of sex as manifested by erections.

We have already stressed the importance of the adolescent's being encouraged to present his own difficulties and taking them directly to the physician. The physician appears to have two primary functions in helping such children. The first is the manner of gaining rapport. Rapport with the adolescent depends on a series of phenomena. One, of course, is acquaintance and the establishment of this acquaintance over a period of time. Often this is already evident in the case of the pediatrician who has followed the child over many years. The physician confronted with an adolescent for the first time must recognize that the child is not going to confide in him quickly and that he must take his time in probing the feelings of such a child. Since one of the difficulties through which the child is going has to do with the establishment of independence, the physician will avail himself of the opportunity to treat the child as though he were a young adult, to see him separately and independently, and to establish with him a new kind of relationship rather than that of the accompanied child of the younger years. Such an approach to rapport is particularly important with any child in whom one senses a conflict between him and his family. It is obvious that one cannot dismiss nor neglect the family, but to separate the family and child is often quite crucial.

Second, the physician has a major role in clarifying the growing situation and helping the child to understand something about himself. It is remarkable how confused the minds of such adolescents are about the simplest facts of their own bodily build, bodily hygiene, and the changes that are manifesting themselves in the growth process and the evolution of sexual maturity. Throughout their lives children have been given a variety of tales about growth and sexual maturation, so that they enter adolescence full of all kinds of odd notions, which become exaggerated as their own growth proceeds, makes them awkward, and leaves them with a new body which they are not quite used to.

In a very simple fashion then, the physician has a new opportunity to try to clarify what these changes mean, how the body can be used, and what the limitations and dangers of physical activity can be. For example, as both boys and girls turn to organized athletics, they become very concerned about "health" and especially about foods. Extremes of dieting or food faddism are common. It becomes a real task to sort out the various ideas about the relation of foods to health that lie behind these fads. Teachers, coaches, and peers supply the child with odd concepts that leave him bewildered. Clarification is warmly welcomed by the adolescent.

We have also mentioned the numerous fantasies that children carry with them from early periods in life that exhibit themselves at the adolescent stage. It is necessary for the physician who is dealing with adolescents to be extremely aware of this fantasy life. It is by no means enough to understand the physical changes that growth brings. One must equally understand the manner in which the child's fantasies separate him out from little children and adults alike, make him uncomfortable in the presence of adults, and lead to his great need for peer relations and peer status.

It is not necessary that the physician learn the entire lingo of adolescent life, inasmuch as it changes so rapidly. However, the child aligns the physician in his mind either with the authoritarian aspects of adult life or with the "squareness" of adult life. There will be added difficulty in modifying the feeling relations and worries that the child has about the impact of the authoritarian, unfeeling, unthinking, and unaware adult generation. In particular, the physician cannot permit himself the moralistic, overbearing attitude that is so easy to fall into when pushed by the bizarre, vacillating, and quickly changing comments of the adolescent. In the relationship of the physician to these particular patients, it is necessary to be stable, consistent, and firm, and yet not be authoritarian. It is amazing how many of the children who act rebellious, who seem most bizarre and unusual in their clothes, talk, and manners, are seeking a stable element in the adult world with which they can identify.

Since the major developmental task of later adolescence is the establishment of an adult identity, it is important that the physician be one person who can present them with an adequate example to which they can cleave. Such an example is a valuable piece of prevention.

Two major groups of severe symptomatology present themselves during this stage of life. One is the active and serious flowering of the psychotic process which came early to the attention of psychiatric diagnosticians and was labeled dementia praecox. Chapter 21 discusses the psychotic process in detail.

The other is the serious problem of delinquent behavior. The physician's role in the latter can be extremely important in relationship to some individuals. Since delinquency is committed by various children for quite different reasons, it is important that the physician try to sort out and assist other authorities in understanding those children who need special attention. The physician's role in clarifying the intellectual status, the physical status, and

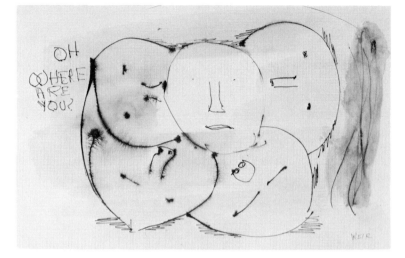

Fig. 20-1. To define who one is and who one is not is a major task of growing up.

the individual emotional status of any one child can be of major value in trying to attack the problem of this child's place in the delinquent drama. Every child involved in delinquency is entitled to a personal appraisal of his own body, personality, and intellect in order to see if there are correctable features that might modify his need to so strongly rebel against home, family, society, and community. Such an appraisal is a proper and appropriate role of the physician.

The subject of delinquency, however, emphasizes most clearly the limitations of the role of the physician. Whereas he can be of assistance to an individual, it takes the larger forces of law and community agencies to deal with the gang behavior of adolescence, as well as the major difficulties that certain children face in school. What seems important is that the physician be available for the personal appraisal of the child. He can then freely contribute his findings, recommendations, and understandings to the other authorities, particularly the legal ones, who are concerned and responsible for the protection of the community as well as for caring for the individual child.

PART IV

SPECIAL PROBLEMS

21

THE PSYCHOTIC PROCESS IN
CHILDHOOD

In recent years it has grown apparent that certain children are much more disturbed than those with the milder emotional difficulties discussed in the earlier part of the book. Furthermore, their symptoms of withdrawal, bizarreness of behavior, and changes in thinking closely resemble the symptoms of the adult psychotic. These children pose very serious diagnostic problems, since at the present time there is a greater interest in increased modalities for treatment as well as in some newer interest in prevention. Full-blown cases pose serious therapeutic problems that cannot be handled in the ordinary medical setting.

THE INFANT

The earliest demonstration of serious withdrawn behavior in children is seen in the type of child whom Kanner, some twenty years ago, described as suffering from early infantile autism. This diagnosis refers to a group of children whose behavior is characteristically altered from the time they are born. Parents see these children as lacking the customary responses of infancy in that they do not respond with the usual social smiles and noises to the cuddling, fondling, and handling of the parents. The parents often describe them as children who are "hard to love." They seem indifferent to the general care of adults. Such children continue to grow in a relatively normal fashion as measured by motor development. Some of them develop speech early and even precociously, but others are brought to clinical attention because of major delays in the speech area. At all times, however, they manifest a cold remoteness and indifference to people around them. Their interest tends to focus on *things,* and frequently their history reveals that they spend a great deal of time preoccupied with tiny objects. At such times they are seemingly content within themselves and seem not to need the administrations or help of others. In fact, when their preoccupations are interfered with, they act rebellious and angry.

Such a serious picture can at times be detected during the first few months of life. Observation in the physician's office suggests an unresponsive child who seems to care little about the things that are done to him. The parent talks about the child's seeming lack of warmth or response. We are indebted to Kanner for noting that the parents of these children tend to be rather aloof, ungiving individuals. It may be that the combination of an unresponsive child and an ungiving parent produces this difficulty. It is not clear what role constitutional factors play in the problem.

The diagnostic appraisal includes a differentiation from the slowly developing retarded child or the child who has suffered from possible damage to the central nervous system. Most autistic children demonstrate adequate intellectual capacity although at times impaired by the functional nature of their disorder. The pediatrician is in a unique position relative to these children. They are rarely seen by the child psychiatrist prior to the second birthday and often not until later. Because of the possibility of altering the development of so serious a disease, a detailed history of one such situation follows:

When George X. was first seen at two and one-half months of age, he was a spindly, worried-looking infant with a vacuous stare, flabby muscles, and pale, thin skin. His hands and feet were cold and slightly moist. He followed objects visually but did not smile and was unable to hold his head steady. His mother reported that he was let alone when he cried. She carried him fastened to an infant seat. He was left alone as much as possible by the mother, who was pleased with his quietness. He subsisted on two meals a day.

George "slept" from 8:00 p.m. to 11:00 a.m., when the mother would enter his room quietly and observe him sucking his thumb. He would be bathed and given his bottle and returned to his crib, where he would occasionally waken and cry softly but would be left "undisturbed." He was fed a second time at 5:30 or 6:00 p.m. and again returned to his crib. Mrs. X. remarked that she was relieved to have such a quiet baby this time. Her first child, a girl eighteen months older, had had colic. Her only concern had been with George's bowels. He would go thirty-six to forty-eight hours before having a bowel movement. She had used suppositories from the time he was one to six weeks old, and "malt" had been added to the formula.

The pregnancy had occurred without intentional plans for or against it, and it was medically uncomplicated. Delivery had been normal, with vertex presentation, and birth weight had been 10 lbs., 6 oz. George had been described as normal at birth. Records from the hospital of his birth showed no neonatal difficulties or abnormalities of any kind. At two weeks he had weighed 10 lbs., 2 oz., and at eight weeks, 13 lbs., ½ oz. He presented no physical abnormalities on routine evaluation, and neurological evaluation demonstrated no specific abnormalities except for his failure to hold his head steady, the poor muscle tone, and cool hands and feet.

Mrs. X., age twenty-eight, had received a degree in Education but had never taught school because of her marriage which had occurred immediately following graduation. She was an intelligent, neat, but somewhat unattractively groomed woman. Significant elements in her own past history were not elicited in the early contacts. Her general manner was one of supercasualness, giving her the superficial impression of being quite comfortable. She showed some lack of appropriate facial expression, and there was hesitancy and guarding of her speech with a lack of voice inflection which suggested underlying and depressive elements. When one spoke to her, it was difficult to be sure how she was responding. The only feeling shown was that of worry which appeared as she discussed George's bowel movements.

In her interaction with George, several features were notable: First, she brought him to the pediatrician fastened to an infant seat in which she continued to hold him, thus preventing direct physical contact with him; second, she rarely presented her face within his view but most of the time looked away from him. There was a minimal amount of handling and a real hesitation in picking him up. When the immunization shot was given and he cried slightly, the infant seat was patted as a soothing gesture.

Comment. It was felt that George was showing deviant development which required emergency consideration, but it was acknowledged that for successful approach to this patient some kind of meaningful relationship with the mother must be established. At this point, it was not known what had contributed to the mother's need to isolate herself from this child. The tentative hypothesis was that she wished to avoid the occurrence of colic which had been so difficult for her to manage with her first child.

Efforts to effect change were made by two methods: first, by demonstrating actual care of the infant and talking about it as it was being demonstrated; and, second, by direct educational measures with the mother. The demonstration with the infant consisted of taking the infant off the infant seat; holding him in the examiner's lap; looking at, smiling, and playing with him; manually stimulating his skin; and, most of all, attempting to elicit the smiling response by face-to-face viewing. Throughout this demonstration the examiner would say, speaking to George but indirectly to the mother, "You see my face and I see yours and we can smile." "Oh, you do like to make noises." "What can you do now with your hands?" "Do you like to be rocked?" "It is fun to suck your thumb," and similar statements.

The mother was first reassured about the bowel movements. She continued discussing this for some time, and the examiner empathized with the concern that a mother has about so many things she is confronted with in her children, like colic in the first·baby and the bowel movements with George. He spoke of the many things there are to learn and how difficult life is for a mother who has a baby with colic interfering with her sleep and making her whole situation different. The mother's own present life situation was discussed. Her needs for sleep and recreation and relief from the family were emphasized and then, almost casually, the baby's needs for stimulation, for being awakened for additional feedings and for closeness to a warm, moving human body (rather than an infant seat) were mentioned in connection with the child's needs for general sensory stimulation as a way of augmenting growth. The examiner maintained a good eye-to-eye contact with the mother throughout the discussion, and her thoughts and feelings about the various comments which the examiner made were invited. The first visit lasted twenty minutes.

A second visit occurred when George was three and one-half months old. The mother spoke with a little more animation and indicated that George was now taking three meals a day, she was bathing him and playing with him more, and he now slept from 7:00 p.m. to 7:45 a.m. Improvement in all areas was noted. George smiled on presentation of a human face. His mother was wondering whether he had "poor metabolism" but was no longer concerned about bowel movements. When the shot was given, she held George over her shoulder and patted him. He was now able to hold his head steady and was beginning to use his hands, reaching out for objects. But there was still minimal face-to-face contact with the mother.

Over the next few months, George's development was carefully surveyed by the physician, utilizing the same methods that had been utilized in the first hour. Mrs. X.'s relationship with her older child, with whom she had considerable difficulty around aggression, was explored. The mother's concern about expressions of aggression, anger, and disappointment was emphasized as much as the child's need for free exploration of the environment. Throughout these interviews, Mrs. X. established a firm conviction in the helpfulness of her visits and became extremely attentive to the recommendations made by the pediatrician. As she, herself, had suggested earlier, her relationship with George improved, and she said she enjoyed him more than she did his older sister. In fact, the focus of concern now was around the older child and the problems of a determined and stubborn two-year-old.

When last seen, George was twenty-seven months old. He walked and ran, and his speech was characterized by short phrases with appropriate voice inflections and gesturing. He seemed to be a happy, loving child, established close contact with other people, and had developed some manual skills which included stacking blocks, turning pages, and writing with a crayon. His physical development was normal. He was turning out to be rather tall, and he was a husky, well-built youngster with good muscle tone and good coordination. He was showing the usual crying on separation from his mother when baby-sitters were used. His sleep had been uninterrupted, and he had been successfully toilet trained without resistance.

Comment. George's case illustrates the fact that if the early autistic trends are diagnosed and treated early enough, reversal can occur. It seems reasonable to suggest that George's development indicates that when treatment was started early, no serious significant difficulties persisted. Mrs. X's capacity to change her mothering role through supportive educational help from the physician undoubtedly contributed greatly to this. An examination of Mrs. X.'s manner of presenting herself and of what is known about her underlying problems also supports the idea that Mrs. X. was not really a "rejecting" mother but was frightened of her own feelings and required distance from her child in order to feel safe with her own destructive and aggressive impulses. A significant help for her was the physician's capacity to allow her to express openly some feelings of resentment toward her older daughter.

THE OLDER CHILD

Certain children who have seemed comfortably normal during their infancy develop severe behavior symptomatology at various later ages. Usually the changes in behavior take place rather slowly over a period of time. Such children are brought to the attention of the physician because of their strange behavior, which is often noted by individuals outside of the family. Changes may be noticed in the pattern of their peer relations; they may develop bizarre or unusual mannerisms; they may regress in their speech patterns or adopt slang or profane language; and they may begin to be preoccupied with themselves and with very minor and particular interests. One characteristic of these children is a regression of their behavior and withdrawal from all activity contact with their peer society. They develop definite changes in their object relationships and begin to relate less to people than to things.

Some children develop extra interests in sexuality and profanity as a part of this regression process. Such interests are an open and overt expression of the common fantasies of all children. These sick individuals seem to be living out, in a very active and open way, the kinds of simple expressions of sexuality that are common to many children. They masturbate openly; they are prone to indulge in attempts to explore the other sex; and at a later stage they are commonly noted to have overt homosexual or heterosexual acting-out behavior. Such children are severely ill. Their thought processes may be confused. Their capacity to learn is frequently destroyed. They become preoccupied with small things or with some isolated intellectual effort and quickly alienate themselves from the society of their peers by their strange and bizarre mannerisms. Other children mark and note them as strange, "kookie," or "psycho."

Again, the medical problem becomes that of early *diagnosis and intervention*. While it is possible for some of these children to be treated on an outpatient basis, many of them will require residential treatment. In any case, the treatment of the withdrawn, regressed, emotionally disturbed child who falls into the category of childhood schizophrenia or childhood psychosis warrants intensive psychiatric care.

Parents of these children are more than usually willing to accept the referral to a psychiatrist. They are commonly bothered by the degree of change in their child even though they may have been slow in perceiving it. Unfortunately, some of these parents also have disturbances in contact with other people. It is, therefore, difficult for them to see in their child evidences of strangeness of relationship that are so apparent to the outside world. When such children go to school, they stand out in sharp contrast to other children and the diagnosis is usually much clearer. Primarily, they present a problem of evaluation and prompt referral to a treating agency.

22

THE ADOPTED CHILD

A growing interest in certain emotional problems of the adopted child resulted from observations that there appear to be more adopted children in psychiatric treatment than is warranted by their numbers in the population. As of the present, no definitive studies have suggested concrete clues for preventive work. We have known for a long time that there is a very real need to understand quite fully the requirements of parents who wish to adopt a child. Social agencies have made tremendous strides in trying to help potential parents understand what they are doing and then to help them through the early stages of child care.

It has been pointed out, however, that, under the best of circumstances, the adoption of a child puts the family into an artificial situation. There are many concerns related to the mode of talking to the child about his adoption, the fact that some people feel a need to keep it a secret, and so forth. As we have noted earlier, children go through stages in which they are torn between feelings of respect and of anger toward their parents. Many natural children envision an idealized set of "good" parents as opposed to the "bad" parents with whom they are actually living. The adopted child, whose dilemma is of a different order, soon learns that he actually had another mother, so he can fantasize all sorts of feelings about her. She can easily become the "good" mother when his adopted mother seems "bad" to him.

On the other hand, the adopted child is confronted with the serious problem that at one point in his life he was given up. It is hard to know what the feelings of the child towards this realization are. It is well known that beginning in adolescence and going on through early adult life, many adopted individuals make a definitive and exhaustive search for their mother. In some surveys of the problems of adopted children it has been noted that acting-out disorders are more common in this group than the anxious, neurotic types of disabilities seen in other children. The full meaning of this acting-out behavior is not clear.

At the present time medical preventive work would seem to be threefold: one, proper preparation of the parents for parenthood with some understanding of why it is that they are so avidly seeking a child; two, general health care such as would be given to any child and set of parents, emphasizing normalcy in development and the establishment of good relationships; and, three, complete honesty with the child about the fact of adoption. It is well not to overstress this point because many parents go out of their way to suggest that there is something better about adoption than the normal birth process. Such exaggerations always lead to difficulties that the child must face with his friends and acquaintances. Rather, it is better to be simple and factual, but honest, in the presentation of the situation.

There remains a need to understand the balance of forces that impinge on an adopted child. Overprotection, for example, is a common phenomenon in such homes. The likelihood of the child's being an only child may be an important factor. The reaction to the artificiality of the situation may cause the parents to act defensively toward the outside world. They may always be aware that the child originally belonged to someone else. This latter fact has a variety of meanings to different parents. Until we understand this complexity of forces, we cannot develop a clear-cut preventive effort. In many centers the special psychological make-up of the adopted child is under study. It is to be hoped that new clues for his care may result.

23

THE HANDICAPPED CHILD

The diagnostic problems of handicapped children, including those with mental retardation, are often less difficult than the management difficulties which ensue once a diagnosis has been made. Many common mechanisms operate in the minds of parents whose child is handicapped by either physical disability or mental defect. We have noted in Chap. 5 the mother's great concern about the wholeness of her child. When a child is found to be damaged in any fashion, her apprehension rises rapidly, and the management of the situation calls for considerable preventive skill.

It is important that the physician be aware of the common mechanisms that come into play in the manner in which the parents handle their handicapped child. One of the first of these mechanisms is that of guilt. The parents ask many questions about a handicapped child, most of which seek to establish the reason for the occurrence of the difficulty. "What it something I ate?" "Was it something I did?" "Did I take good care of myself?" It is important to be as understanding and helpful as possible in answering such questions, since out of these expressions of guilt grow serious modes of action that lead to further handicapping.

The parents of a handicapped child tend to become extremely overprotective because of their feelings. They set up methods of care for their child that can result only in the child's failure to develop.

In the instance of a disability such as a cardiac defect which may lead to death, this overprotection may be warranted. In the case of many other disabilities, the overprotection merely prevents the child from going through the normal stages of growing and maturation to which he is entitled. It should be clearly noted that except for the disabled part, the rest of the child may grow and mature in a manner comparable to that of his peers.

It is not difficult to recognize these overprotective attitudes in the handling of such children. They are seen very early in the manner in which the children are dressed, fed, and handled. For certain children some protection is needed. The blind child, the deaf child, or the cerebral palsied child needs more than ordinary care. However, it becomes necessary for the physician to assess all other aspects of the child's function and behavior in order to determine how much can be done in spite of the handicap. The parent then can be helped to focus on those areas that are not involved in the handicap rather than to become totally preoccupied with what seems to them the central facet of the child's life.

This overprotection and guilt may give rise to other symptoms of which the physician should be aware. Part of it may be a hostility directed against either the child, the outside world, or the physician himself. Many times parents become angry at themselves for having gotten into such a predicament. They will protest that fate has treated them badly or that the world has given them a bad deal. When things seem to be moving slowly and no progress is occurring in the orthopedic or other management of the handicap, they may become quite angry with the physician, change doctors, or protest loudly about the handling of the child. Such expressions of overt anger are to be expected in the course of the handling of any handicapped child. It is important that the physician be prepared to accept them, understand them, and not be swayed by them.

Certain parents with physically handicapped children become very angry at the child himself. The failure to develop becomes a serious complication of a family life pattern. The child is seen as not only awkward or inadequate, but he seems to challenge the position of the family. We mentioned this earlier in talking about the manner in which parents present symptoms. All of the mechanisms that are used by parents in talking about their children become obvious at such times. Frequently, the children are chided for their slowness in development in the area of the handicap itself. In extreme cases, children are beaten and treated cruelly because of the symptomatology that is a part of their illness.

The physician must see the entire picture as a part of a living situation involving every member of the family. The parents' concern over the handicapped child may lead to deficiencies in the care of their other children. On the other hand, they may neglect the handicapped child and fail to foster what development can occur. The siblings of retarded and other handicapped children often suffer not only by parental neglect, but also because of their concepts of the picture presented to the outside world. Siblings of a defective child are often teased for it, and they become overly defensive and protective. In each instance it is necessary to talk with the individuals involved about their specific feelings. It is not enough merely to point a direction for the handicapped child; it is equally important to know what the family expects, what they want for themselves and other children, and what their feelings of guilt, anger, or impatience may be. Only by allowing them to talk out these situations can a complete understanding be achieved.

In many instances, the physician will do well to seek the help of other agencies in the handling of this family situation. There is a growing body of interest in such family care among groups of social workers associated with the general care of handicapped children. Discussion groups of such parents have been a very worthwhile by-product of the powerful parent groups that have sprung up in connection with each handicapping condition. Although, for the most part, such parent associations are dedicated to the proposition of getting the best care for the afflicted children, it is more important from the medical point of view to use them as vehicles for increasing parent education and assisting parents in understanding their feelings about the handicapped child.

The cultural climate that surrounds the mentally retarded child and his family produces an exaggerated form of the syndrome we have just described. Society has evolved many forms of education and care for these children. The work with the parents of mentally handicapped children has been not so well developed as that with parents of physically handicapped children, partly because the parents themselves then to focus on the child. These children, however, would profit greatly if their parents were better understood and could transfer such understanding to the ongoing care of the child. All of the mechanisms we have described are operative in these parents. Again, the opportunity to talk out problems may well be the best therapy the physician has to offer. Parent groups under medical supervision are most valuable in dealing with the family of the mentally defective child.

EPILOGUE

As a reader you may consider that much of the material in this book is either too repetitious or on the other hand too skimpy. Since the normal processes of life and the relationships between parents, children, and doctors tend not to vary with the years, it is not surprising that the same thing is said over and over again in talking about both treatment and development. On the other hand, it is impossible to go into great detail in a book that is primarily concerned with prevention.

If you are stimulated by the reading of this text to explore psychological development and therapeutic methods more seriously, there are a variety of books on the subject. Erikson's book, *Childhood and Society* and Irene Josselyn's book, *Psycho-Social Development of the Child* provide the best basis for understanding the whole process of development. The standard textbook of child psychiatry is that of Kanner and is a large impressive text which can be used as a valuable reference book. More recently, two textbooks of child psychiatry have appeared and are of value to the physician. The one is by Stella Chess and the other is by Stuart Finch. Many pediatricians will enjoy reading the works of D. W. Winnicott who is referred to in our text. His *Collected*

Works gives an excellent example of a shift of interest in a physician's practices from certain specific concerns relative to physiology to a broader concern with the growing child. It is hoped that these references will be of service and that they will serve as a structure to further reading later on.

INDEX